An Introduction to the Dreamtime

Australian Aboriginal mysticism explained and explored.

Contents

Introduction

The question arises: what is the Australian Aboriginal Dreamtime? The answer to this is obtained via a brief, though circuitous route.

If we, in a strictly non-gender sense, divide human capacity for perceiving reality into masculine and feminine faculties, we very soon learn that 'the real world' is not as easily grasped as we might have hoped—reality is multi-dimensional. Indeed, the masculine, external, strictly material perception proves to be of relatively minor importance. No, this is not to say that one can walk through walls and closed doors without acquiring a bloodied and probably broken nose.

One simple tool that will help us in our quest is to give each of our two faculties a symbol: 1 (One) for the masculine external and 0 (Zero) for the feminine internal. And let us also assert here that all men and all women have both masculine and feminine (1 and 0) perception capacity.

What we know of the relatively minor masculine is that it's a chatterbox and a bossy boots. From the moment we wake up till the time we go to sleep, this egotistical little dictator, made grossly insecure by the physical world's constant threats to our safety, is continuously shouting in our heads: 'mind this', 'be careful of that', 'get real', 'pay attention'. On the other hand, the feminine has long since given up trying to compete with the idiot it has to work with: after all, within the confines of its job description, One is doing as it should. A way in which we might grasp the relativity of these two is to say that where One is a bush telegraph, Zero is a cell phone with Internet capacity. For myself, I would say that Zero gives me, and anyone else for that matter, direct access to the humungous main-frame computer at the centre of the universe—God. And by 'the centre of the universe' I mean the centre of myself—or yourself.

Ancient civilizations everywhere were clearly concerned with the balancing of these two forces. It is *a)* clear that they succeeded and *b)* obvious that this did not result in lives spent in navel-gazing. Our world is strewn with clear and unambiguous evidence that Megalithic Man was a scientific genius.

But it is in the nature of One to abhor compromise; it demands the right to dominate, that is, it thinks SNAGs are wimps. Its most recent and successful rebellion and rise to power was consolidated in the hands of René Descartes (1596-1650) and his horde of Cartesian philosophers. If, they said, you can't touch, taste, smell, hear or see it, then it just isn't there. Later, they came up with the idea of lobotomizing those hapless heretics for whom 'it' would not go away. Cartesian insanity reached its peak when shock troops were sent to countries like Australia to root out the heresy by exterminating the people who clung to it. Yes, at its base, colonialism was an offshoot of One's rise to power, a phenomenon *seeded* at the dawn of the Piscean Age.

In the West, these same heretics came to be known to us as Hermeticists, Cabbalists and Alchemists. The transmutation of lead into gold became a metaphor for balancing the hemispheres of the mind. The alchemist was his own laboratory and he, himself, was the experiment. His Eastern counterparts left us with the concept of balancing the Yin and the Yang. And they all went to their graves telling us that we should make the inner as the outer and the below like unto the above. Today's materialistic and mechanistic world, the fragmentation of religion and subsequent fragmentation of values, the fragmentation of knowledge and, ultimately, the fragmentation of the individual can all be seen as springing from the Cartesian consolidation of One's rise to power.

Its flower, of course, is the bucket of bolts we call a computer. And with this monstrosity, the Cartesians have philosophically shot themselves in the foot, for its basis is the binary system—an integration and utilisation of ones and zeros; it would seem that the below is like unto the above after all.

Yes, dear reader, the Australian Aboriginal Dreamtime is an alchemical, hermetic, Jungian type of psychological process by which balancing the one and the zero gives us a total grasp of reality. And furthermore, the Dreaming is not yesterday, today or tomorrow—it is timeless; it is now and it is forever. Through it, all mind and soul is connected; it is one.

So, dear brother and sister, read on and remember to keep the faith and keep on dreaming.

Beginning Dreaming

The sticks and horseshoes are respectively men and women, depicted here upon three islands. Very ancient tradition says the people departed the islands to the north of Australia (the Indonesian group) and crossed the Timor Sea to Australia. Recent research has indicated that they had originally lived in the Indian sub-continent but were driven out by the southerly drift of the Arya tribes.

Tradition says a boastful man threw his boomerang across the ocean and claimed it had reached the furthest island on the other side. His claim was, of course, disputed and derided. But the solution was provided by a little boy who cut out the entrails of a koala. He then proceeded to blow into them until they formed a rainbow bridge across the ocean. All the disputants crossed over the entrail bridge and, arriving in Australia, they became the mothers and fathers of the Aborigines.

Frill-necked Lizard

Walek, the frill-necked lizard, led the lizard people of Nelgi Island (fifty kilometres north of Cape York). They had yet to discover fire and their cooking procedures, using sun heated stones, were subsequently long and laborious. But Walek had a sister living in the far-off islands of Papua New Guinea from where smoke was often seen to rise. It was Walek who undertook the long and dangerous journey to his sister's village. At first, she refused him and then gave him a cold coal, but he persisted and finally returned to a hero's welcome with the gift of fire.

Because lizards are connected with thieves (stealing fire) and shape shifting, we might relate this to the little boy who came from nowhere and would never tell anyone about himself. He was very lovable and was adopted by the tribe, but soon all manner of things, except the Tjurunga and other sacred objects, began to go missing. He was eventually caught and was about to have a thrashing administered when a falling spear injured him and he died. His body was covered with bark but the next day it had disappeared. In its place, there was only a lizard.

Waterhole Dreaming

When, in the beginning Dreaming, three beautiful young women came down from the stars to visit the earth, they went walkabout. From time to time they needed to pass water; where they did so, they left sacred pools. If a mortal man should come upon one of these waterholes and drink from it, the liquid would greatly increase his capacity to learn the Dreaming knowledge.

It is this process that took men out of their primal embryonic stage, in which they lived as the Inapatua: formless and shadowy beings with only faint traces of what they would one day become. The Numbakulla were two sky-brothers who, whilst looking down upon the earth, decided to come with their knives and give final shape to these plastic creatures. They turned them into men and women and sent them off to populate Australia.

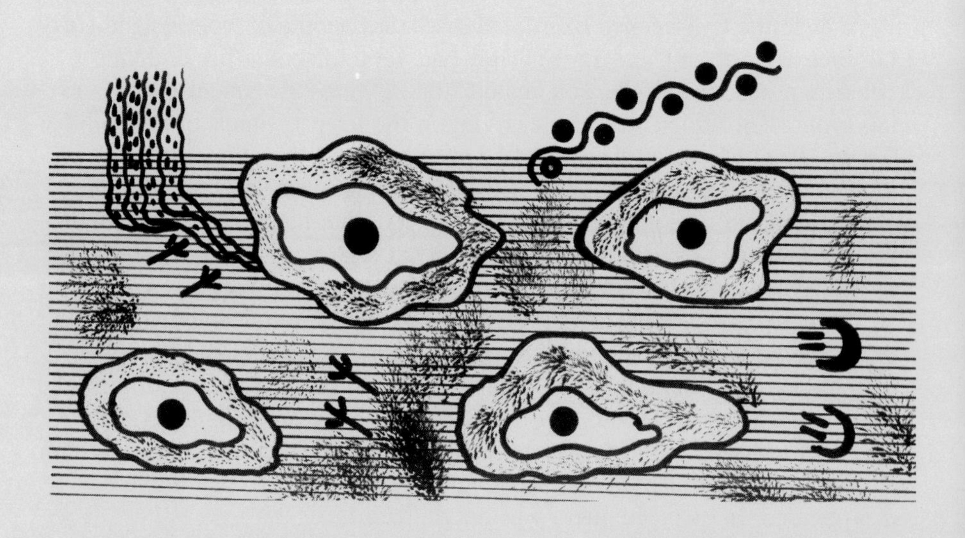

The Birth of Emu

Of the three sisters who came down from the stars of Orion's Belt, two returned and one was obliged to stay on earth and play the role of Tya (the earth spirit). Because the emu is a flightless bird, it symbolizes the third sister's being a prisoner on earth. But the emu is a dowdy, ill mannered and ill-tempered creature, not the best choice for the incarnation of the ultimate female.

The first thing Emu created was the Tnatanja Pole, it was covered in down and reached up to the stars. But she left it in the care of Termite Woman, whereupon it was given to breaking and snapping where she had eaten into it. It was this constant falling and erection that ultimately shaped the Australian landscape.

Brolga

Long ago, when all had been made but was in total darkness, Brolga and Emu disputed as to the need for light in the world. Brolga said no, things were fine as they were. Emu said the animal people were forever bumping into each other and were unable to find their things when they had put them down. Brolga got very angry and clipped Emu's wings, making her a flightless bird. Emu avenged herself by tossing a brolga's egg into the sky. The egg exploded and became the sun. Now everybody can daily admire the beauty and colours of the great work of the Sky Father.

This story is virtually a replica of the stories found commonly among the Amerindians. In their tales, Emu is replaced by Grandmother Spider who, of all the animal people, was the only creature able to bring the gift of light into the world.

The Birth of the Sun

The sun was born of a brolga's egg which exploded after Emu tossed it into the sky, and from this explosion the rainbow also came into being. The rainbow is invariably associated with water which, because it falls from the sky and fertilizes Mother Earth, is both the seed and wisdom of Father Sky. The rainbow was termed pulwaiya (father's father), but it was both the divine phallus and the divine womb. As the essence of all life, it accompanied the aged Kunapipi when she went on her great walkabout.

Another story says that Punjel waited patiently for the Great Byamee to finish making everything; their home in the Milky Way was, in the meantime, extremely cold. Meanwhile, in anticipation of Byamee creating fire, Punjel built a very large woodpile. He then sat and amused himself by watching Emu and Eagle-Hawk scrapping over ownership of a carcass down on earth. Emu won the prize and an angry Eagle-Hawk tossed one of her eggs into the sky. It hit the huge woodpile, which then burst into flames and became the sun.

Mother Earth and Father Sky

In ancient nature religions, it is common to find the Goddess (earth spirit) in the form of a trinity or as triple-headed. In Aboriginal tradition, as previously mentioned, three women descended from the stars and two of them later returned; these are depicted here by the circles of dots. It is at the equinoxes (when the sun crosses the celestial equator) that Father Sky (the sun) and Mother Earth are joined as man and woman.

The task of separating these two passionate lovers was left to the magpies who, unable to use their wings, had tried walking around the cramped space between earth and sky. Thousands organised themselves and, with sticks in their beaks, they pushed against the sky in unison. Initially it was a very hard task, but it got easier as they made more and more space. Ultimately the sky split asunder and light flooded the world.

Yarandoo

It was a time when food was in short supply and many survived by catching and eating the rat kangaroo, but one man remembered the words of the great Byamee (he who brought the law from the All Father): ‘The rat kangaroo is forbidden flesh.’ So it was that this righteous man would sooner starve than break the law. In his wanderings he approached a tree, hoping he might find food there. A yowee spirit descended from it, picked up the man and took him into the tree, which uprooted itself and rose up to the heavens. It then manifested as the constellation called Yarandoo (the Southern Cross).

Rat kangaroos seem to be associated with star making, as is the mischievous bird Wahn, the crow who tricked Pewingi, the swamp hawk, into jumping on a bunch of echidna spines he had planted in a rat kangaroo’s nest. But once they had grown into Pewingi’s claws, this only helped him to better catch the rat kangaroo. Byamee ultimately put an end to his mischief by turning him into a star. The crows have never since ceased to laugh at Wahn’s comeuppance—they greet each morning with Wah, Wah, Wah.

Crocodile Dreaming

This creature, wherever he appears, is a revered totem. He was a close companion of the Seven Sisters (in the Milky Way) when, as the result of a curse, they lived as water girls. But his real claim to fame is that each month, at full moon, he begins to tear strips from the moon man until he has completely devoured him. Whereupon, the moon man is reborn and the cycle begins again.

Bahloo, the moon, was also a victim of Wahn the crow. Bahloo lived in a cave way up in the side of a hill where he made girl babies and sent them down to married women in any quantity they required. Because he would not let Wahn make the boy babies, Wahn tricked him into climbing a tree for a feed of grubs. The trickster crow then uttered an incantation that made the tree grow up to the stars where Bahloo is now still stuck.

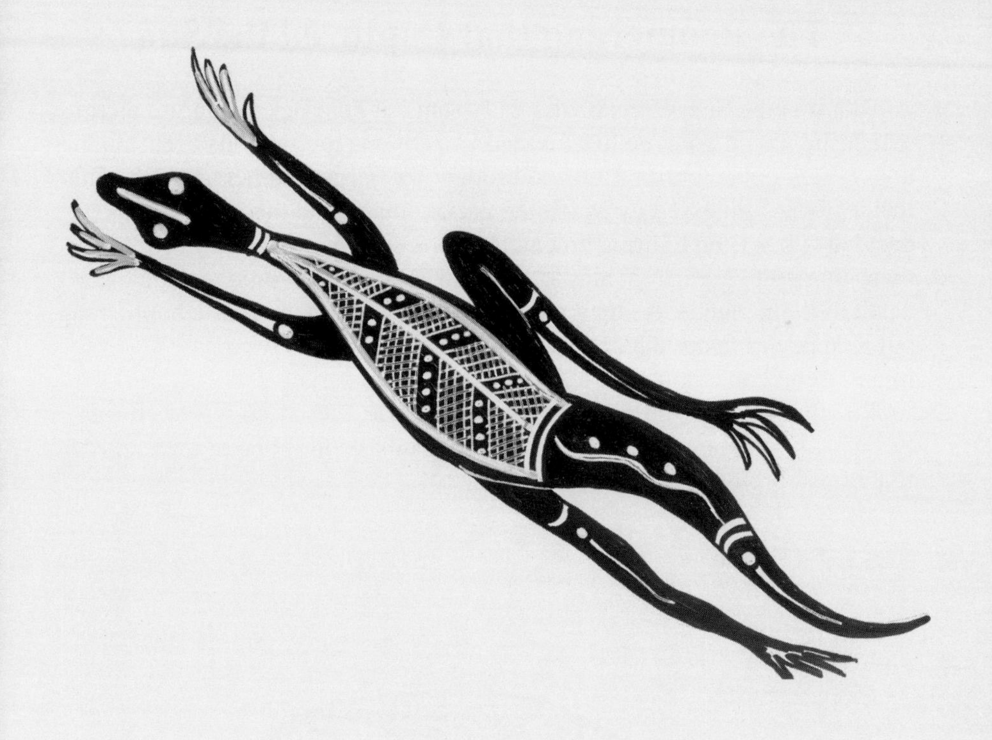

Goanna and Snake

These two creatures make frequent joint apperances in Aboriginal art. This is because, in her feminine aspect, Snake is an excavator of riverbeds and Goanna man was the inventor of the canoe. As an expert tree climber, he stripped the bark from a messmate tree and patiently sewed it into a boat which gave fishermen access to the deeper and more rewarding parts of the rivers.

Goannas were originally very industrious creatures who had arrived with the first migration from the thousand islands in the canoe belonging to Whale. But as they moved south through Australia, they gave up planting and reaping the vegetables they loved so much and took to preying upon small and defenceless creatures.

After childbirth, women were restricted to remaining by a fire; Snake, being a water spirit, would not molest them if they were close to the fire.

The Boomerang that Captured the Sun

Bila was the Sun Woman who daily sent out her dogs to capture victims, which she would cook on her fire and eat. On one momentous occasion, her dogs wiped out an entire tribe and brought the corpses to her as a gift. This incident was witnessed by Muda the gecko and Kudna the lizard, who decided it was time to bring an end to Bila's shenanigans. They set off on their journey to her camp, all the while swearing they would avenge the death of their friends. As they approached her she reached for a boomerang, but Kudna was faster than Bila and, when struck by his weapon, she turned into a fireball and vanished, leaving the world in darkness.

Fearful of the gloom and what they had done, these two fellows began throwing boomerangs to all points of the compass until one of them, thrown to the east, brought back the sun.

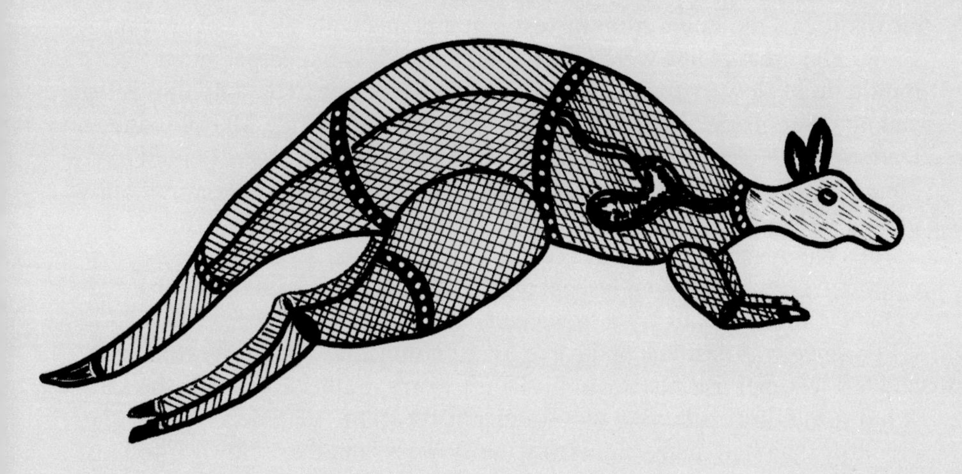

Kangaroo's Legs

When he first arrived in Australia on Whale's canoe, Kangaroo walked and ran just like any other four-legged creature, but he quickly found that men were eager to hunt him as a source of food. On one occasion, he spied a hunter approaching with spear in hand and took off into the bush, fully believing that his four legs would be faster than the man's two, but he was wrong and the chase persisted all day. It only ended when darkness fell. Kangaroo lay collapsed in an exhausted heap when he saw the hunter lighting a fire. 'I had better move quickly and quietly before the light exposes me,' said Kangaroo to himself. He raised himself on his hind legs to minimize the noise, and stealthily hopped away. Realising how easily he was moving, he decided that two legs—as with men—were obviously better than four. From that moment, his hind legs got stronger and his forepaws got shorter. That's why the kangaroo is as he is today.

Marmoo's Jealousy

Byamee had made the world and both he and it were at peace. Crystal-clear streams ran down from majestic mountains with peaks covered in snow. The great plains were covered with a lush green carpet and a multitude of flowers painted every imaginable colour. The only things that had not been made were the birds and insects. Meanwhile Marmoo, the Dark Spirit, looked down on this scene in jealousy and rage. 'I could have done better in less time,' he told his wife. Her simple response was: 'Show me.' 'I will,' he said, 'but first I must destroy Byamee's handiwork.'

In a cave where none could see, Marmoo created a vast horde of creeping, crawling, flying insects which, when he released them, proceeded to ravage the land and lay it to waste.

Byamee was desolate and came to see Nungeena, the spirit-woman he had left to supervise his creation. 'Don't worry, Father Byamee,' she said. 'I hid some flowers behind that waterfall.' Working with deft fingers, she quickly fashioned many birds from the flowers, and these flew off to feast upon the insects whose ravages the earth was able to quickly overcome.

CORONE RECORDS

in England and Wales

Jeremy Gibson and Colin Rogers

THIRD EDITION

The Family History Partnership

This edition published 2009 by
The Family History Partnership,
PO Box 502,
Bury, Lancashire BL8 9EP

Email: sales@thefamilyhistorypartnership.com
Webpage: www.thefamilyhistorypartnership.com

First edition, 1988, reprinted 1989, 1992.
Second edition, 1997, reprinted (with minor amendments) 2000.
Both published by the Federation of Family History Societies

ISBN 978 1 906280 13 0

Typeset from computer discs prepared by Jeremy Gibson
and printed by Parchment (Oxford) Limited

Cover illustration from the most famous-ever investigation of death,
'Who killed cock robin?'

To Thomas Garner Rogers, 1896-1988

Acknowledgements

It is right first to acknowledge our different spheres of responsibility. Although his name comes second, the suggestion to compile this Guide came from Colin Rogers. For the first edition, the bulk of the work was done by him, composing the questionnaire sent to repositories, collating the replies and dealing with most of the correspondence. He also corresponded with the Coroners' Society, wrote the Introduction and compiled the Bibliography and Glossary. In the second edition he analysed the replies received from freshly circulated repositories. These resulted in much additional information about deposits of modern records, though these are mainly closed to researchers.

Jeremy Gibson arranged the Guide in its present form, and, for this latest edition, has trawled the Internet. Again, most additions to holdings relate to recent records and not all may have been located (news of others always welcome). As before, most remain closed for 75 to 100 years, so are of little currrent relevance.

We both owe much gratitude to Dr R.F. Hunnisett, whose name is synonymous with research into the earlier coroners' records, as a glance at the Bibliography will show. For the first edition, he kindly read the Introduction and Glossary, making many valuable suggestions, and so redrafted the section on sources in the Public Record Office (now The National Archives) itself that his authorship deserves acknowledgment.

Obviously we have also, as always, received a great deal of help and encouragement from archivists throughout England and Wales (the Guide is confined to these countries as comparable records do not appear to have been generated elsewhere in the British Isles).

Amongst coroners themselves, for the first edition we appreciated advice and interest from Dr J.D.K. Burton, Secretary of the Coroners' Society, Mr L. Gorodkin, H.M. Coroner for Manchester, and Dr D.J. Harte, H.M. Coroner for Bedfordshire.

Although coroners' records are generally of peripheral use to family historians, it is gratifying that new editions continue to be required.

J.S.W.G. and **C.D.R.**

CONTENTS

Coroners' Records, England and Wales:

INTRODUCTION

by Colin Rogers

This is a first attempt to itemise all extant coroners' records in England and Wales now in public repositories. It incorporates lists made by Dr Hunnisett (1959: see Bibliography) for the medieval period, and by the Royal Commission on Historical Manuscripts (card index). The present Guide is intended not only for genealogists but also for a number of other potential users of these records such as historians, archivists, sociologists, criminologists, police, and for the coroners themselves, who are not always aware of the records which their offices have generated over time. Because of the nature of the material, it is important to stress that:

a) there are special rules concerning access to records less than 75 years old at the time of the research (see below);

b) transfer of records from most coroners to repositories is ongoing – the most recent dates quoted in this Guide are correct for early 1997; and

c) material in some areas is regularly being destroyed once it is over 15 years old (see below). Some records in this Guide may therefore no longer exist at the time of the intended research.

Background

Since 1194 it has been the duty of coroners to investigate the circumstances of unnatural, sudden, or suspicious deaths, and of deaths in prison; good accounts of the working of the office may be found in the works of Dr R.F. Hunnisett for the earlier periods, Dr J.D.J. Havard for a critical assessment of the whole period, Burton *et al*, and G. Thurston for its contemporary operation, and the current edition of *Coroners' Rules* which provides the regulations. The following notes may help to put the records themselves into perspective.

The status, functions, relationship to local government, and public image of the coroner have evolved over eight hundred years, changes reflected not only in the type of records but even in their survival rate. The functions of the medieval coroners reflected their relatively high social standing – in the earliest years the county coroners should have been knights – and financial importance. Apart from holding inquests on dead bodies, they received felons' abjurations of the realm, heard appeals of felons, and promulgated outlawries in the county court. But, despite what medieval statutes and treatises say, they did not normally deal with treasure trove (or with wreck of the sea and royal fish) until after the Civil War.

Until 1926, all inquests were held with a jury which was more akin to the grand jury rather than to that of the petty (trial) jury, and could vary in number from 12 to 24. Numbers were reduced to 7-11 in 1926, with a proviso that not more than two may dissent.

Most coroners were elected by freeholders until 1888, since when they have been appointed by local authorities. Their jurisdiction was theoretically over a whole county, until geographical divisions were drawn in more modern times, although from the thirteenth century each coroner had at least an informal district of his own; others acted for areas of specific privileges – boroughs or liberties. Contemporary county guides or directories should list coroners for particular periods. The jurisdictions shown in an *Atlas of Coroners' Districts*, 1888-1902, are listed on pages 14-15.

From the fourteenth century, their status and functions declined, so that by Tudor times almost their only function was holding inquests on dead bodies; from 1487, they could receive a fee of 13s.4d. for each inquest resulting from homicide. The sole qualification, for six hundred years (1340-1926), was to be a landholder.

From June 1752 coroners were allowed one pound for every inquest held outside gaols and ninepence a mile for their journey from their home to the body, provided that 6 the place where the body was found contributed to the county rates; their fee for holding inquests in gaols could not exceed one pound. The Municipal Corporations Act of 1835 extended this system of payment, with modifications, to boroughs. Magistrates had the right to question their claims for fees, and claims were sometimes refused. This obstacle to the effectiveness of the work of the coroners (who until 1926 were not required to have either medical or legal qualifications) extended beyond 1836 when funds were authorised for medical post-mortems for the first time. Dr Havard believes that this professional jealousy between coroners and magistrates had its origins in a misinterpretation of medieval statute, seized upon by magistrates who were jealous of the right which they shared with coroners to commit for trial. The number of inquests dropped in the mid-nineteenth century, just as a growing number of social commentators were revealing the inadequacies of registration systems in an age of urban growth.

From 1860, when county coroners first became salaried, the right of magistrates to block fees was broken, and we enter the era when the increasing forensic skills of police and the medical profession could at last be put at the disposal of the coroner, and the loopholes in the documentary relationship between coroners and registrars of death began to be closed. In the twentieth century, both of these developments have been carried further, and society looked to the coroner's office not only for the truth behind untimely deaths, but increasingly for the lessons to be learnt from individual tragedies.

Present day coroners and their records

Today, 'the work of the coroner' is briefly described for the general public in a small Home Office guide of that name, available from all register offices. Cases are referred by the police (who often provide the staff for the coroners' officers), the medical authorities, or registrars of death:

when no doctor treated the deceased during the last illness;
when the attending doctor did not see the patient within fourteen days before death, or after death;
when the death occurred during an operation or before recovery from the effects of an anaesthetic;
when death was sudden and unexplained or attended by suspicious circumstances; or
when the death might be due to an industrial injury or disease, or to accident, violence, neglect or abortion, or to any kind of poisoning.

The social, as well as forensic, purpose behind these enquiries is evident from the list. The coroner might establish that death was, after all, due to 'natural causes'. We are not sure that this phrase has ever been defined in the relevant legislation; but if medical examination, either by a local doctor, or (after removal of the body) by post-mortem does not indicate that the death was suspicious or unnatural, it becomes a 'non-inquest' case, an order for burial or cremation can be issued, and the registrar directed to make an entry in the register of deaths (using the words on the coroner's certificate, as the coroner is the informant – though he has not had to sign in person since 1859). In cases where an inquest is held, the registrar includes the verdict in the entry. The inquest itself will be adjourned *sine die* if anyone has been accused of murder, manslaughter, causing death by reckless driving, complicity in another's suicide, or infanticide.

Most inquests since 1926 have been without a jury, and there were no juries during the Second World War. Inquests are, however, in public, unless there is a threat to national security, and newspapers have reported cases for over two hundred years. For this reason, enquirers are normally directed to newspaper reports for particular cases, for which exercise another Guide in this series, *Local Newspapers* (new edition in preparation), will prove very useful. In general, you are more likely to find a newspaper report than a coroner's record during the hundred years before the Second World War.

'Properly interested persons' can question witnesses, and see (or purchase copies of) the notes later. Such persons include close relatives of the deceased, those having an insurance interest, anyone who might have contributed in any way to the death, a chief officer of police, a person appointed by a government department to attend, and anyone else appearing to the coroner to have a proper interest.

Coroners are given some discretion in three matters which significantly affect many records included in this Guide.

Destruction of records. A schedule of destruction is laid down in Home Office Circular 250/1967. While they are within the definition of public records, for whose preservation the Lord Chancellor is responsible, and all are open to the public after 75 years (treasure trove after 30 years), many will not survive those 75 years. Once 15 years old, the records can be 'weeded' – destroyed or sampled, for example – by the individual coroner concerned.

Certain classes of record are scheduled for permanent preservation – the indexed registers of deaths reported, all papers dated before 1875, papers relating to treasure trove, cases illustrating in any significant way contemporary coroners' practice, and cases relating to general public, scientific, forensic, social, local, industrial or unique historical interest. A random sample of other papers may also be kept. Equally, because HO Circular 250/1967 is permissive in this respect, a coroner need not destroy any records, a course which many of them choose to take.

Access to records. Public access to coroners' records is governed by the Public Records Act 1958 as amended by the Public Records Act 1967, s.44, and Coroners' Rules (1984) Rule 57. By an order of the Lord Chancellor, under s.5 of the 1958 Act (Instrument No. 68, *Access to Public Records*, 16 April 1984), records relating to reported deaths are closed to the public for 75 years, though many archivists still seem to be applying the former 100 year closure rule. Anyone who, in the opinion of the coroner, has a *bona fide* research interest may be given access to closed records no matter where the records are stored. However, the coroner will have due regard for privacy, and for the avoidance of propaganda or mischief. The coroner is not bound to supply reasons why an application for access is refused. For further observations on this issue, see Thurston's *Coronership* (1976), pp.153-6.

Preservation. Once the records are five years old, they may be transferred to a repository recognised and designated by the Lord Chancellor's Department, and in any case should normally be so transferred before they are 30 years old. A few coroners choose not to deposit, and their records do not appear in this Guide. Most are only too pleased to do so, and retain control over record destruction. Additionally, since the Blair Peach case, many coroners return documents which had been provided to assist in the determination of which witnesses to call; those documents are not part of the records.

However, this situation leaves the archivists with two major problems. The sheer bulk of the material puts great pressure on the storage capacity of some record offices, and so there is the rather unedifying result that a small minority of archivists must press the coroners concerned to have records in their custody destroyed as soon as they are 15 years old. Coroners have also been known to deposit objects which would have been regarded, before 1846, as deodands, which must surely be regarded as the most macabre contents of a record office.

The second problem relates to access, partly by those who do not understand the current rules of access and of record preservation, but particularly by close relatives of the deceased, for whom archivists must sometimes act as untrained and often unwilling councellors. For these reasons a few archivists expressed some doubt about the wisdom of compiling this Guide.

However, with later editions it is gratifying that no repository has refused information on their modern records, as had been the case with the first edition twenty years ago.

It must be stressed to all potential researchers that both coroners and archivists have varying attitudes concerning access to modern records, but that in all cases of requests for access to records of deaths less than 75 years old, the initial approach must be made to the coroner's office, not to the repository concerned.

The content of records

Some records, particularly the recent ones, are standardised nationally, as prescribed in the current *Coroners' Rules* (1984). Others are less precise, and some in this Guide are described in calendars using the words of archivists rather than of coroners. Only manuscript holdings are normally included; Home Office circulars, and publications of the Coroners' Society (founded 1846) may also be found deposited in a few areas. Unless indicated, it should be assumed that no records except the registers of deaths reported will have been indexed.

The following Glossary aims to serve as an introduction to the contents of the records under their normal appelation, but there is no guarantee that the description of contents will be universally applicable, especially before the twentieth century. Those asterisked are illustrated in Burton *et al* (1985) and Thurston (1976).

GLOSSARY

Appeal. Private accusation of felony.
Autopsy. See Post-mortem.
Bill or Voucher. County coroners (1752-1860) and borough coroners (1835-1887) were able to submit claims for fees and travelling expenses (one pound per inquest and ninepence per mile) to local authorities, payable from the rates, for inquests duly held. These claims often include the names of the deceased, dates and places of inquests, casuses of death and verdicts. Because many are located among the Quarter Sessions records, not all repositories have listed them separately for this guide.
Certificate after inquest*. Notification to registrar indicating date of inquest (with or without post-mortem), verdict, all details required to complete the death entry, marital condition, date of birth of surviving spouse, details of accident or injury causing death, details of burial or cremation order, and where appropriate details of criminal proceedings.
Certificate 'E'*. Order for cremation, inquest or non-inquest, showing name of deceased, sex, age, date and place of death, and sub-district in which death is to be registered. A detachable portion is sent, after cremation, by the registrar of cremations to the registrar of death.
Daily record. Sheets giving names of deceased, together with all data required for Home Office returns *(q.v.)*.
Deodand. From earliest times, the object deemed to have been the cause, by its movement, of a death by misadventure. At various times it (or its monetary value) was given to the church, the king, the lord, or the immediate dependants of the victim. It was abolished in 1846, by which time people were being killed by locomotives!
Deposition. Statement from witness to assist proceedings of an inquest.
Enquiry. Any case referred to the coroner - see Burton *et al* (1985).
Exigent, writ of. Summons to appear in the county court. Non-appearance resulted in outlawry.
Form 100. See Notification to registrar.
Home Office returns*. Annual statistical statements showing the number of deaths reported, by sex; number of inquest and non-inquest cases; analysis of verdicts by age and sex of victim; number of exhumations, and treasure trove inquests; results of inquests adjourned for criminal proceedings; and salaries.
Inquest, book/register of. Indexed lists of inquest cases showing date, name, address, place of death. It is probable that some of the earlier 'inquests' in this Guide contain the full file, including depositions, verdicts, etc. Inquests can be held on lost or irrecoverable bodies, and into deaths abroad.
Inquisition*. Summary of the inquest, showing date, name, time, cause and place of death, verdict, details required by the registrar of deaths, and signatures of jurors.
'Inquisition' may sometimes be used synonymously with 'inquest', and until modern times might be the only record of an inquest. From 1487, many were forwarded, via the assize justices, to the King's Bench: see general section below. The term is also used for a form indicating that a named person is committed for trial from a coroner's court.
Non-inquest. Case reported to a coroner who, after medical advice, decides that an inquest is unnecessary. Since autopsies were first allowed in these cases in 1926, their numbers have doubled, while the number of inquests has remained fairly static.
Notification to registrar (Form 100, or 'Pink Form')*. Part A informs the registrar of deaths that no post-mortem is to be held on a deceased person whose name, age, date, place, and cause of death are shown; Part B follows a post-mortem, with its results. The counterfoil gives name, age, cause, date and place of death, who reported the case, and whether Part A or B had been completed.

Order for burial*. Authorisation for the body of a person, with name, and place and date of death, to be buried following view or examination. It is given to the person responsible for burial, or for the recording thereof; in modern times there is a detachable portion, which is passed to the registrar of deaths following the burial.

Order to remove body (for inquest)*. Authorisation to remove a body from its place of death, or current resting place, to a place suitable for post-mortem examination. Name, age, and places given. Holding inquests in dwelling houses or licenced premises, common in the last century, is forbidden.

Passing. Used in the Merseyside area for cases involving no post-mortem.

Pink Form - see Notification to registrar.

Post-mortem report*. Follows the autopsy, and summarises its findings. Gives name, age, height, rigor mortis, nourishment, surface marks, estimated time of death, internal examination of head, thorax, abdomen areas, and all organs; date, time, place, observers, and pathologist/doctor responsible. Post-mortems on non-inquest cases have been allowed only since 1926.

Recognizance to witness/juror*. Statement of amount of fine payable if a witness or juror fails to appear at prescribed proceedings.

Register of deaths (reported)*. Normally gives (time and) date of report, name, address, age, and sex of deceased, cause of death, whether an inquest was held and if so what verdict. Can also include police responsible, place of post-mortem and inquest, and names and addresses of jurors. A name index should be included.

Removal of body out of England and Wales*. Part A, retained by the coroner, shows name of deceased, name and address of person making the request, and dates of issue. Part B is an acknowledgment of receipt, and is given to the applicant. Part C is a notification, to the registrar of deaths, of Parts A and B, giving name of deceased, and date and place of death. This procedure has applied, since 1926, irrespective of the cause of death.

Return - see Home Office returns.

Roll. In medieval times (mostly 1229-(c.1330) records of inquests which were 'enrolled', so that several cases were presented to the visiting justices in eyre in the same document. Most of those which survive, however, were of later date, prepared for visitations by the Court of King's Bench, until their perambulations stopped in the early fifteenth century. Names, times, circumstances of death are given, and deodands where appropriate; published editions may give the resulting cases followed up by the justices.

Summons to jurors*. Direction to a named juror to appear at a prescribed time and place.

Treasure trove. Report of an investigation into whether gold or silver objects have been hidden, when their true owner was unknown. Statements of expert witnesses and the outcome of the case are given. See Hill (1936).

Voucher. See Bill.

Warrant to summon jurors*. Direction to the police to summon a specified number of jurors at a prescribed time and place.

BIBLIOGRAPHY

Readers may find the following helpful on the general subject of coroners. The titles are additional (with the exception of Gross, 1896) to the topographical references incorporated in most county sections.

W. Baker, *The Office of Coroner* (1851).

British Medical Association, *Deaths in the Community* (1964 and 1986 editions).

Brodrick Report: *Death Certification and Coroners*, Command Paper 4810 (1971).

J.D.K. Burton, D.R. Chambers and P.S. Gill, *Coroners' Inquiries* (1985).

J.S. Cockburn, *Calendar of Assize Records: Introduction* (see also under 'Assize Circuits' and under Essex, Hertfordshire, Kent, Surrey and Sussex).

Coroners' Rules 1984 (Statutory Instrument No. 552).

Departmental Committee report, *Coroners*, Cd.5004 (1910).

J.B. Edge, *Some Remarks upon the Office and Duties of Coroners* (1872).

G.A. Fereday, *Coroners' Cases* (1957).

J.S.W. Gibson, B. Langston and B.W. Smith, *Local Newspapers 1750-1920*, 2nd edition (2002).

C. Gross, *Select Cases from the Coroners' Rolls 1265-1413, with a brief account of the history of the office of coroner*, Selden Soc. **9** (1896) (Note. The individual cases are identified under county sections).

J.D.J. Havard, *The Detection of Secret Homicide* (1960).

Sir G. Hill, *Treasure Trove in Law and Practice* (1936).

R.F. Hunnisett, 'The origins of the office of coroner', *Trans. R. Hist. Soc.*, 5th series, **8** (1958).

R.F. Hunnisett, 'Pleas of the Crown and the coroner', *Bulletin of Historical Research*, **32** (1959).

R.F. Hunnisett, 'The medieval coroners' rolls', *American Journal of Legal History*, **3** (1959) (lists all the then known rolls).

R.F. Hunnisett, *The Medieval Coroner* (1961) (see also under Sussex)/

R.F. Hunnisett, 'The reliability of inquisitions as historical evidence', in D.A. Bullough and R.L. Storey, eds., *The Study of Medieval Records: Essays in honour of Kathleen Major* (1971).

R.F. Hunnisett, 'Early chancery records: rolls and files', *Journal of the Society of Archivists*, **5** (1975).

R.F. Hunnisett, 'The importance of eighteenth-century coroners' bills', in E.W. Ives and A.H. Manchester (eds.), *Law, Litigants and the Legal Profession* (Royal Hist. Soc. Studies in History **36**, 1983).

Jervis on Coroners (various editions since 1829).

P. Knapman and M. Powers, *Law and Practice of Coroners* (1985), being the 3rd edition of Thurston (1976).

G. Thurston, *The Coroner's Practice* (1958).

G. Thurston, *Coronership* (1976).

E. Umfreville, *Lex Coronatoria: or, the Office and Duty of Coroners* (1761; second edition by J.B. Grindon, 1822).

F.J. Waldo, 'The ancient office of coroner', *Trans. Medico-legal Soc.*, **8** (1911).

For the most up-to-date information about the work of the coroner, see websites:
<www.coronersofficer.org.uk>
<www.direct.gov.uk/en/Governmentcitizensandrights/Death/WhatToDoAfterADeath/DG_066>
<www.hta.gov.uk/about_hta/faqs/coroners_faqs.cfm>
<www.justice.gov.uk/whatwedo/coroners.htm>

ASSIZES CIRCUITS AND SERIES REFERENCES OF INDICTMENTS

The following notes are largely based on T.N.A. Legal Records Information Leaflet **30: Coroners' Inquests.** <http://www.nationalarchives.gov.uk/catalogue/rdleaflet.asp?sLeafletID=175>

From 1558 until 1971 England and Wales were divided into various 'Circuits'. The counties included in each until the mid-nineteenth century (when there were various regroupings), are listed below. In some cases T.N.A. lists give separate references for individual county bundles for each year (or group of years). When they are listed merely by circuit, the counties will nevertheless be individually gathered within each year.

Oxford: Berkshire, Gloucestershire, Herefordshire, Monmouthshire, Oxfordshire, Shropshire, Staffordshire, Worcestershire. **ASSI 5**, 1663 on.

Midland: Derbyshire, Leicestershire, Lincolnshire, Northamptonshire, Nottinghamshire, Rutland, Warwickshire. **ASSI 12**. Main series from 1880 on only. **ASSI 80** is a small collection, 1652-88 for single assizes: Derbyshire 1662, 1667, 1687; Leicestershire 1653, 1656; Lincolnshire 1652, 1653, 1654, 1660, 1679; Northamptonshire 1659, 1660; Nottinghamshire 1663, 1664, 1682; Rutland 1667, 1685; Warwickshire 1652, 1668.

Western: Cornwall, Devon, Dorset, Hampshire, Somerset, Wiltshire. **ASSI 25**, from 1801 on only.

South Eastern or Home: Essex, Hertfordshire, Kent, Surrey, Sussex. **ASSI 35**, from 1559 on (see also **Norfolk** below). These are the best surviving records, and for the reigns of Elizabeth I and James I (1558-1625) are published in detail in a series by J.S. Cockburn, *Calendar of Assize Records* (a volume per reign for each of the five counties, together with an Introduction which describes and illustrates the records covered). Professor Cockburn has continued the series for Kent to 1688 in four volumes; the first three are already published and the fourth is in the press.The Essex Record Office has a typescript calendar of all Essex indictments to 1715.

Norfolk: Bedfordshire, Buckinghamshire, Cambridgeshire, Huntingdonshire, Norfolk, Suffolk. ASSI 16, 1653-1698. From the 1690's these counties are included in ASSI 35.

Northern: Cumberland, Northumberland, Westmorland, Yorkshire. **ASSI 51**, 1868, 1871 on only; but **North-Eastern** Circuit, **ASSI 44**, has indictments 1607-1890 for Berwick, Durham, Northumberland, Newcastle, York, Bradford, Hull, Leeds, Scarborough, Sheffield.

Great Sessions (1543-1830). All Welsh counties. Surviving records are deposited in the National Library of Wales, Aberystwyth (see under 'Wales').

North and South Wales (1830 on). Welsh counties and Cheshire. North Wales, **ASSI 64**, 1831-1891 (also Coroners' Inquisitions, **ASSI 66**, 1798-1891); South Wales, **ASSI 71**, 1834-1892.

Palatinate of Chester. No indictments survive.

Palatinate of Durham. DURH 17, 1582-1876.

Palatinate of Lancaster. PL 26, 1424-1868.

THE NATIONAL ARCHIVES

by Dr R.F. Hunnisett

There are many records in The National Archives which have not been, or cannot be, listed by county.

The great majority of coroners' inquests in The National Archives are on the files of the court of King's Bench. The various classes of indictments [KB 9, KB 10, KB 11 and KB 12] contain many individual inquests summoned into the court by special writ, but from 1487 until about 1700 coroners handed in all their inquests at the twice-yearly assizes. Those which resulted in trials at assizes for murder or manslaughter are, from 1559 until the present century, so far as they survive, on the Assize Indictment files for the relevant counties (see T.N.A. Legal Records Information Leaflet **30: Coroners' Inquests**), and note on circuit coverage and survival of records below); some inquests with other verdicts are also filed with them and, in some circuits, among Depositions. Normally, however, inquests not resulting in trials at assizes were forwarded to King's Bench, and there are thousands of them for every county among the records of that court – most in Ancient Indictments [KB 9], but some in other indictment files, in a small artificial class of Coroners' Inquisitions [KB 13] of c.1740-1820, and among the Plea Side Miscellanea [KB 140].

Inquests on which pardons were based were summoned into Chancery and many are on the Chancery Recorda files [C 260]; the inquests are from the thirteenth century to the early seventeenth, and they are often recited verbatim in the pardons as enrolled on the Patent Rolls [C 66].

Writs for the election of coroners are in three classes of Chancery Files: Tower and Rolls Chapel Series, Certificates of Election of Coroners and Verderers [C 242], 1283-1633; Tower and Rolls Chapel series, Various Counterwrits [C 261/1-3], Ric II - Ed VI (c.1377-c.1553); and Petty Bag Series, Chancery Files [C 202], 1570-1921, detailed lists of which have been published by the List and Index Society (**116-7**, **169-71**).

ATLAS OF CORONERS' DISTRICTS, 1888-1902

[T.N.A., HO 84/3]
shows the following:

Beds. County; Ampthill Honor; Bedford Borough.

Berks. Districts: Abingdon; Newbury; Reading; Wantage; Hungerford. Boroughs: Newbury; Reading.

Bucks. Districts: Aylesbury; Beaconsfield; Newport Pagnell; Winslow; Buckingham. Ampthill Honor.

Cambs. Cambridge County; Ely, Northern and Southern Divisions. Cambridge Borough.

Ches. Districts: Knutsford; Chester; Stockport. Halton Fee Manor. Boroughs: Chester; Birkenhead.

Corn. Districts: Western; Truro; Bodmin; Liskeard; Launceston. Penzance Borough.

Cumbd. Districts: Eastern; Western. Egremont Lordship. Cockermouth Honor. Seignory Liberty and Honor of Millom. City of Carlisle.

Derbys. Derby County. Appletree Hundred. Tutbury Honor. Scarsdale District. Repton and Gresly Hundred. Derby County Borough.

Devon. Districts: Honiton; Crediton; Barnstaple; Okehampton; Stoke Damarel; Totnes; Dartmouth; South Molton. Borough: Barnstaple; Exeter; Plymouth and Devonport; Tiverton.

Dorset. Districts: Northern; Eastern; Southern; Western. Liberty of Badbury and Cogdean; Liberty and Hundred of Cranborne; Gillingham Liberty; Sherborne and Yetminster Liberty.

Durham. Districts (Wards): Chester; Darlington; Easington; Stockton.

Essex. Districts: Eastern; Southern and Western; Metropolitan; Romford; Sokens; Writtle and Roxwell Manor. Colchester Borough.

Glos. (and **Bristol**). Districts: Lower; Upper; Stroud; Forest; Tewkesbury. Boroughs: Bristol; Gloucester.

Hants. Districts: Southampton; Fareham; Winchester; Basingstoke; Andover; Christchurch; Fordingbridge; Ringwood. Boroughs: Winchester; Southampton; Portsmouth. Isle of Wight.

Heref. Districts: Leominster; Hereford. City of Hereford.

Herts. Districts: Bishops Stortford; Hemel Hempstead; Hertford; Hitchin; Royston; St Albans.

Hunts. Hurstingstone Liberty. Norman Cross Hundred. Leightonstone Hundred. Ramsey Liberty. Toseland Hundred.

Kent. Districts: Cranbrook; Greenwich; Romney; Sittingbourne; Ashford; Tonbridge; Sandwich; Hythe; Deal. Liberty of Romney Marsh. Boroughs: Gravesend; Rochester; Maidstone; Canterbury; Margate; Ringwold; Dover; Folkestone.

Lancs. Districts: Preston; Blackburn; Salford; Rochdale; West Derby; Bolton; Lancaster. Furness Liberty. Manors: Hale; Prescot; Walton-le-Dale. Boroughs: Liverpool; Manchester; Bolton; Blackburn; Burnley; Oldham; Wigan.

Leics. Districts: Southern; Northern; Framland. Borough of Leicester.

Lincs. Districts: Lincoln; Kirton; Caistor; Louth; Boston; Grantham; Stamford; Spalding. Boroughs: Lincoln; Grantham; Grimsby; Stamford.

London. Districts: Eastern; North-Eastern; Central; Western; Penge; Southern; South-Western; South-Eastern; Duchy of Lancaster (Clapham and Savoy portions). Tower Liberties; City of London; Southwark Boro; City of Westminster; Queen's Household (Palaces).

Middx. Districts: Eastern; Central; Western. Duchy of Lancaster Liberty.

Monm. Districts: Abergavenny; Monmouth; Newport; South Monmouth. Chepstow Manor (Franchise Coroner).

Norfolk. Districts: Lynn; Norwich; Thetford. Clackclose Hundred and Half Hundred. Duchy of Lancaster Liberty. Duchy of Norfolk Liberty. Boroughs: King's Lynn, Norwich, Yarmouth.

N'hants. Districts: Eastern; Middle; Western. Northampton Borough. Nassaburgh Hundred (Soke of Peterborough).

N'hmbd. Districts: Northern; Southern. Boroughs: Berwick upon Tweed; Newcastle upon Tyne.

Notts. Districts: Nottingham; Newark; Retford. Boroughs: Nottingham; Newark.

Oxon. Districts: Central; Northern; Western; Southern. Boroughs: Oxford; Banbury.

Rutland. Districts: Northern; Southern.

Salop. Districts: Pimhill; Ford; Stottesden; Purslow; Bradford North; Bradford South; Bridgnorth; Ludlow; Oswestry. Boroughs: Shrewsbury; Wenlock.

Som. Districts: Northern; South-Eastern; Western. Boroughs: Bath; Bridgwater.

Staffs. Districts: Hanley; Uttoxeter; Stafford; West Bromwich; Wolverhampton. Burton-on-Trent Manor. Boroughs: Hanley; Newcastle; Walsall; West Bromwich; Wolverhampton.

Suffolk. Districts: Lowestoft; Stowmarket; Newmarket and Haverhill; Sudbury. Liberties: St Etheldreda; Bury St Edmunds; Duke of Norfolk's. Boroughs: Bury St Edmunds; Ipswich.

Surrey. Districts: Kingston; Reigate; Guildford; Boroughs: Guildford, Croydon.

Sussex. Districts: Rye; Lewes; Horsham; Chichester. Bosham Hundred. Hastings Rape. Robertsbridge Hundred. Boroughs: Hastings; Brighton. Liberty of Pevensey Bay.

Warw. Districts: Northern; Central; Southern. Boroughs: Birmingham; Warwick.

Westmd. Districts: East and West Wards; Kendal and Lonsdale Wards.

Wilts. Districts: North Wilts.; Mid Wilts.; South Wilts.; Devizes (Borough of). Salisbury Borough. Corsham Manor.

Worcs. Districts: North; Middle; South; Dudley (Staffs.). City of Worcester.

Yorks. East Riding. Districts: York; Selby; East Riding. Liberties: Holderness; Howden. Borough: Kingston upon Hull.

Yorks. North Riding. Districts: York; Northern; Pickering; East Riding; Langbaurgh East, North, West; Whitby Strand Liberty. Scarborough Borough.

Yorks. West Riding. Districts: York; Selby; Doncaster; Rotherham; Wakefield; Halifax; Craven; Northern. Ripon Liberty, Bowland Liberty or Wapentake. Pontefract Honor: Pontefract Honor, Wakefield District. Boroughs: Doncaster; Bradford; Leeds; Sheffield; York.

WALES

Anglesey. County.

Brecknocks. (or Brecon). Districts: Northern; Southern. Crickhowell and Tretower Liberties.

Caernarvons. Districts: Northern; Southern.

Cards. Districts: Cardigan; Lampeter; Aberystwyth.

Carms. Districts: Eastern; Western. Kidwelly Honor. Carmarthen Borough.

Denbighs. Districts: Denbigh; Wrexham.

Flints. County. Maylor Hundred.

Glamorgan. Districts: Northern; Eastern; Western. Ogmore Manor. Boroughs: Cardiff; Swansea. Gower and Kilvey Liberties.

Merioneth. County.

Montgomerys. Districts: Machynlleth; Newtown; Welshpool; Llanfyllin.

Pembrokes. Districts: Upper; Lower.

Radnors. Districts: Eastern; Western.

NOTES ON PRESENTATION

1. Without a detailed examination of the individual documents, it is not normally possible to ascribe a calendar year to many medieval records. As the regnal years given in calendars are therefore shown in this guide, some readers might find it useful to have the following table, showing the date on which the monarchs began the first year of their reign.

Henry III	28 October 1216	Henry IV	30 September 1399
Edward I	20 November 1272	Henry V	21 March 1413
Edward II	8 July 1307	Henry VI	1 September 1422
Edward III	25 January 1327	Edward IV	4 March 1461
Richard II	22 June 1377		

An over-all indication of the approximate years covered by each group of medieval rolls is shown against such entries.

2. Details are as supplied by archivists, or have been extracted from entries shown in various published or manuscript calendars.

3. Within each English county, listed in order of pre-1974 configurations, the records are arranged in three groups: ***Medieval*** (generally pre-sixteenth century); ***Sixteenth*** (or ***Fifteenth***) ***to Nineteenth Centuries*** (which occasionally include some early twentieth century material); and ***Modern*** (generally twentieth century, but occasionally some late nineteenth century records also). Within these groups the records are listed by repository. It is possible, therefore, that records for individual places will appear in more than one entry.

4. Archivists were not asked to supply details of the geographical boundaries between coroners; some were kind enough to do so, however, and this information has been included. See also the late nineteenth century jurisdictions listed from *the Atlas of Coroners' Districts* on pages 12-13.

5. Similarly, we have included reference numbers when these have been supplied.

6. An asterisked date signifies that some or all of the records are, at the time of writing, normally subject to the 75 year closure rule (see above).

BEDFORDSHIRE

Medieval

Published

R.F. Hunnisett, *Bedfordshire coroners' rolls* (1265-1380), Beds. Hist. Record Soc. **41** (1961).

C. Gross (1896) [for JUST 2/46;2/1-4(pts)] (1264-76).

The National Archives [class JUST 2/].

County. Rolls 49-56 Hen III [46], 53-56 Hen III [1-2], 1-3 Ed I [2-3], 4 Ed I [4;255/1A;265], 9-11 Ed I [6] (1264-83).

Bedford Borough. Rolls 28-32 Ed I [5], 12 Ed II - 4 Ed III [272] (1299-1331).

Gonville and Caius College, *Cambridge.*

County. Roll 1-4 Ric II [Roll 26] (1377-81).

Bedfordshire & Luton Archives & Record Service, *Bedford.*

County. Coroners' roll 1377-8 [Fac 23].

Sixteenth to Nineteenth Centuries

The National Archives. See page 13 for coroners' records in King's Bench, Assizes and Chancery.

Bedfordshire & Luton Archives & Record Service.

County. Appointments, fees etc 1865-1966* [CO/App].

Fees, salaries, etc 1837-98, 1929, 1960-73 [CO/Fin 1,2,5].

Inquest books 1831-1930* [CO/Inq 2/1].

Inquest accounts *re fees* 1851-1921 [CO/Inq 2/2].

General office matters, 19th-20th centuries (legislation, circulars, Coroners' Society etc) [CO/Off 1-7].

Modern
(asterisked dates usually subject to 75-year closure)

Bedfordshire & Luton Archives & Record Service.

County. Deaths reported 1959-93 [CO/Inq 1/1].

Railway accidents 1924*-30* [CO/Inq 1/2].

Home Office returns 1952*-63* [CO/Inq 1/3].

Daily records 1972*-80* [CO/Inq 1/4].

Files 1972*-80* [CO/Inq 2/3].

Inquiries, include. archaeological 1965*-81* [CO/Inq 3/1,2].

Notices for moving bodies out of England 1952*-1961* [CO/Inq 4]

Statistical returns 1980*-91* [CO/Inq 7].

Personal papers 1951*-1986* [CO/Per].

Inquisition photographs 1955*-67* [CO/PH].

Treasure trove 1965*-92* [CO/Inq 2/4].

North District. Correspondence 1956*-65* [CO/Fin 3].

Daily records 1939*-72* [CO/Inq 1/4].

Files 1952-72 [CO/Inq 2/3/NB].

South District. Daily records 1944*-72* [CO/Inq 1/4].

Files 1964-72 [CO/Inq 2/3/SB].

Luton files 1950-72 [CO/Fin 4].

Bedford. Daily records 1945*-74* [CO/Inq 1/4].

Files 1952-74 [CO/Inq 2/3/BB].

BERKSHIRE

Medieval

Published

Description of Wallingford rolls 9-11 Ed II (1315-18) in Hist. MSS. Comm. 6th report, Appx. p.584.

The National Archives [class JUST 2/].

County. Rolls 36-40,43-4,46-8 Ed III & 2-7 Ric II [7,mm.1-4], 5- Ed III & 4 Ric II [8], 5-7 Ric II [9,mm.2-6], 8-21 Ric II [10,mm.1-2.4-11] (1362-1398).

Liberty of the Abbot of Reading. Rolls 1-8 Ric II [9,m.1], 19-21 Ric II [10,m.3](1377-98).

Reading Borough. ?-18 Ric II [255/16] (? - 1395).

Berkshire Record Office, *Reading.*

Wallingford Borough. Files of inquisitions, abjurations, appeals 1291-1308 (various) [W/JCf 1-3].

Coroners' rolls prepared from the above, 1291-1305, various, incl. deaths in castle prison [W/JCr 1-2].

Appeal rolls *c.*1300-1320 (gaps) [W/JCa 1-6; also on MF 323].

Memoranda, incl. deaths in prison 1316-17 [also on MF 323], natural deaths 1317, inquisition 1320, list of jurors *c.*1320, confession to murder 1507 [W/JCm 1-6].

Appeal rolls and memoranda 1300-20, various [W/JCa 1-6; W/JCm 1-4, all on MF 323].

List of jurors c.1320 [W/JCm 6].

Memorandum of confession to murder at Brightwell 1507 [W/JCm 5].

Sixteenth to Nineteenth Centuries

The National Archives. See page 13 for coroners' records in King's Bench, Assizes and Chancery.

Berkshire Record Office, *Reading.*

Berkshire County:

Account book, listing cases 1775-1814 [D/EX 1412/1]; indexed [T/B62].

Treasurer's accounts, with claims, listing cases 1834-59 [Q/FA 3/1]; indexed [T/B62].

Boroughs and County Divisions:

Abingdon Borough (under 1555 charter the mayor was ex-officio coroner. The surviving records are fragile).

Inquisitions 1688-1781 [A/JC1-4; all above on MF 43]; indexed.

Hungerford Borough (here the annually elected constable was *ex-officio* coroner and escheator).

Inquisitions 1811-1926*, except 1852-54 [H/JC 1/1-6; to 1877 on MF 153]; indexed.

Newbury Borough. Inquisitions (catalogued) 1836-62 [N/JQ 10/1-2]; indexed.

Note book listing cases 1839-46 [N/JQ 10/3].

Berkshire continued

Newbury District. Account book, listing cases 1855-1949* [COR/N 2/1-2].
Registers, detailing cases 1856-70 [COR/N 1/1-2].
Inquisitions (cat'd) 1866-1914 [COR/N3/1-47]; indexed.
Annual returns 1870-1901 [COR/N 4/1-26]
Reading Borough. Inquisitions 1839-1912 (cat'd) [R/JQ6/1-6]; indexed.
Wallingford Borough. List of cases 1756-1836 [W/JQS1-2]; indexed.
Wantage Division. Inquisitions (cat'd) 1875-1912 [COR/WT1/1-38]; indexed.
Notifications of death 1883-1912 [COR/WT2/1-23].
Annual returns with notes 1975-1906 [COR/WT3/1-5].
Miscellaneous 1871-1921 [COR/WT4/1-7].

Index to all above inquisitions available [T/B85]

Modern
(asterisked dates usually subject to 75-year closure)

Berkshire Record Office, *Reading.*
Abingdon District. Annual returns 1894-1940*.
Inquisitions (uncat'd) 1936-42*.
Maidenhead District. Miscellaneous papers 1913-1947*
Inquisitions (uncat'd) 1924-53*
Newbury District. Accounts, listing cases 1855-1949* [COR/N2/1-2].
Inquisitions (cat'd) 1866-1914 [COR/N3/1-47].
Inquisitions (uncat'd) 1914-49*.
Police reports 1915-21 [COR/N5/1-8].
Reading District. Inquisitions 1918 (one only), 1930-55*.
Slough District. (in Berks since 1974) Inquisitions (uncat'd) 1974-80* (then in E. Berks.).
Wantage District (see last section).
East Berks. Inquisitions (uncat'd) 1957-90*.
Registers of deaths reported 1966-90*.
South Berks. Inquisitions (uncat'd) 1954-73*.
Register of deaths reported 1953-65*.
West Berks Inquisitions (uncat'd) 1974-92*.
Registers of deaths reported 1965-90*.
Newbury Borough Inquisitions (uncat'd) 1950-72*.
Register of deaths reported 1953-65*.
Windsor Borough Inquisitions (uncat'd) 1910-18, 1934-48*.
Registers of deaths reported 1953-74*.

BUCKINGHAMSHIRE

Medieval

Published
J.G. Jenkins, 'An early coroner's roll for Buckinghamshire', *Records of Buckinghamshire* **13** [for JUST 2/14(pt)].
Lesley Boatwright, *Inquests and Indictments from late Fourteenth Century Buckinghamshire: The Superior Eyre of Michaelmas 1389 at High Wycombe.* Bucks. R.S. 29 (1994) [JUST 2/13 and JUST 2/14, KB 9/5].
C. Gross (1896) [for JUST 2/12(pt)].

The National Archives [class JUST 2/].
County. Rolls 22-4,26-7 Ed III [11,mm.1-12], 36-43 Ed III [12], 47-51 Ed III [13], 1-13 Ric II [14,mm.1-19,21] (1348-90). Part published.
Rector of Ashridge's Liberty of Pitstone. Roll 5, 10 Ric II [14,m.20] (1386-7).

Sixteenth to Nineteenth Centuries

The National Archives. See page 13 for coroners' records in King's Bench, Assizes and Chancery.

Centre for Buckinghamshire Studies, *Aylesbury.*
County. Bills: Treasurers' rolls [Q/FR] 1752-1817 include coroners' claims for expenses, most giving names of inquest subjects, and verdicts.
High Wycombe Court book, incl. coroner's court [microfiche only: M40/35-39] 1761-1834.

Bedfordshire & Luton Archives & Record Service.
Honour of Ampthill (Bucks. parishes).
Statement of inquisitions 1854-1917 [HN uncat. boxes 106,137].

Modern
(asterisked dates usually subject to 75-year closure)

Centre for Buckinghamshire Studies, *Aylesbury.*
South Bucks. Registers of reported deaths 1970*-1982*.
Daily records 1938*-46*.
Files of inquests 1935*-96*.
Mid Bucks. Registers of reported deaths 1962*-1981*.
Files of inquests 1931*-81*.
North Bucks. Registers of reported deaths 1967*-84*.

CAMBRIDGESHIRE

Medieval

Published

C. Gross (1896) [for roll JUST 2/17(pt)].

C. L'Estrange Ewen, *The Families of Ewen of East Anglia and the Fenland* (1928) [for rolls JUST 2/18(pt) and 2/22(pt)].

See also *The East Anglian* N.S. **13**.

The National Archives [class JUST 2/].

County. Rolls 7-12 Ed III [15-17], 14-39 Ed III [18-19], 44-8 Ed III [256/1-4], 37-43 Ed III [21], 42-5 Ed III [22], 44-7 Ed III [273], 49 Ed III - 7 Ric II [24] (1333-84).

Cambridge Borough (right to coroner in 1256 charter). Roll 43 Ed III - 4 Ric II 23 (1369-81).

Sixteenth to Nineteenth Centuries

Published

'Did your ancestors serve on the Coroners' Election Committee?', *Cambs. FHS Jnl*, **4**.8, Winter 1984. Re. Wisbech.

The National Archives. See page 13 for coroners' records in King's Bench, Assizes and Chancery.

Cambridgeshire Record Office, *Cambridge.*

Cambridge City. Inquisition books 1826-33, 1836-1866.

Inquisitions 1836-72, 1885.

Papers re murder prosecution 1864.

Inquests about fires 1850-58.

Correspondence re deodand 1842.

Appointments of deputies 1837-48.

Accounts 1845-83.

Papers 1837-64.

Modern
(asterisked dates usually subject to 75-year closure)

Cambridgeshire Record Office, *Cambridge.*

County (excl. City of Cambridge):

Daily record: registers of inquests 1894-1950*.

Inquisitions 1922*, 1925*-39*.

Isle of Ely (Northern Division only):

Notes of inquests 1914*-22*.

Depositions 1933*-44*.

Deposition books 1926*-44*.

Police and medical reports 1943*-52*, 1957*-59*.

Inquisitions 1939*-64*.

Treasure trove 1934.

Quarterly reports 1906-53*.

Corrrespondence 1933*-52*.

It is believed that records of the Southern Division of the Isle of Ely, and later records of the County of Cambridge with which it was merged, were destroyed following water damage in the 1950s.

Cambridge Town. Inquisition books 1959*-69*.

Inquisitions 1940*, 1945*-83*.

Certificates after inquest 1978*-83*.

Enquiries not requiring post-mortem 1978*-83*.

Registers of deaths reported 1958*-70*.

Post-mortem reports 1945*-6*, 1948*-83*.

Photographs as exhibits 1945*-58*.

Notices of removal of bodies out of England 1928*-1946*.

Statistical returns 1915*-52*.

Accounts 1942*-58*.

Counterfoils of the following:

Notifications to registrar (after inquest and without inquest) 1944*-58*, 1963*-64*; order for burial 1948*-58*, 1962*-65*; certificates for cremation 1944*-58*, 1962*-64*; and removal acknowledgments 1946*-53*, 1961*-64*.

CHESHIRE

Medieval

The National Archives *[class JUST/2].*

County (including Flintshire).

Inquisitions: temp. Ed III (1327) to Anne (1714) [CHES 18/1] (32 only).

Macclesfield Hundred. Eyre roll 15 Ed III [Pal. of Chester 13,m.68] (1341-2).

Sixteenth to Nineteenth Centuries

Published

T.R. Forbes, 'Coroners' inquisitions from the county of Cheshire, England, 1817-39 and 1877-78', *Bulletin of the History of Medicine* **59**, pt. 4 (1985).

The National Archives

County (including Flintshire). Inquisitions: temp. Ed III (1327) to Anne (1714) [CHES 18/1] (32 only); temp. Geo I (1714-27) [CHES 18/2] (50); temp. Geo II (1727-60) [CHES 18/3]; 1794-1850 [CHES 18/4-45].

Halton. Inquests and returns 1848-49 [DL 46/23].

See also page 13 for coroners' records in King's Bench, Assizes and Chancery.

Cheshire & Chester Archives & L.S., *Chester.*

Chester City (coroner as early as 1289, confirmed by 1300 charter; abolished in 1983).

Inquisitions (incl. examinations of witnesses and warrants to summon juries) 1519-1839 [QCI] (indexed).

Inquests 1839-1927* [QSF].

Stockport Archive Service, Central Library.

Stockport District. Register of deaths reported 1851-56 [MF].

Local Studies Unit, Manchester Central Library.

Stockport District. Register of reported deaths 1851-56 [MF, Local History library].

Wilmslow. Orders for burial 1824-29 [MF].

Cheshire continued

Modern
(asterisked dates usually subject to 75-year closure)

Cheshire & Chester Archives & Local Sudies, *Chester.*
Central Cheshire. Daily record books 1922*-57*.
West Cheshire. Daily record books 1952*-74*.

Chester City. Inquests 1839-1927* [QSF].
Daily record 1937*-66*.
Register of deaths reported 1953*-63*.
Depositions and inquisitions 1935*-62*.
Police photographs 1935*-41*.
Financial papers and accounts 1935*-72*.
Correspondence 1929*-65*.
Home Office circulars and returns 1939*-73*.
Post-mortem reports 1935*-41*.
Reports of sudden deaths 1939*-62*.
Inquisitions 1943*-52*
Police reports of deaths 1942*-51*
[All above except first, ref. QC.]

Liverpool City Library (Record Office), *Liverpool.*
Birkenhead. Inquest registers 1898-1972* [COR/K/1/1-17].
Register of deaths reported 1953*-75* (indexed) [COR/K/2/1-7].
Wirral. Inquests and photographs 1974*-83*.
Daily record 1974*-81*.
Register of inquests 1898-1972*.
Register of deaths reported 1953*-75*.
Wallasey Borough. Inquest registers 1937*-76* [COR/Y/1/1-21].
Police inquest books 1957*-67* [COR/Y/2/1-5].
Daybooks 1969*-77* [COR/Y/3/1-2].
Inquest papers 1950*-74* [COR/Y/4/1-18].

Greater Manchester Record Office,
56 Marshall Street, Manchester M4 5FU.

Stockport, Tameside and **Trafford** (part). See note under Lancashire, page 28.

CORNWALL

Sixteenth to Nineteenth Centuries

The National Archives. See page 13 for coroners' records in King's Bench, Assizes and Chancery.

Cornwall County Record Office, *Truro.*
Truro Borough. 14 warrants (most with inquests, evidence, or jury lists attached) 1812-33 [B/T 486-502].

Cornwall continued

Modern
(asterisked dates usually subject to 75-year closure)

Cornwall Record Office, *Truro.*
Mid-Cornwall (Bodmin). Complete files of depositions 1942*, 1952*, 1962*.
Mid-Cornwall (Truro). Complete file of depositions 1962*.
Selected files of special or local or potential historical interest 1958*-72*.
East Cornwall. Complete file of depositions 1962*.
Selected files of special or local or potential historical interest 1946*-60*.
North Cornwall. Selected files of special or local or potential historical interest 1964*-71*.

CUMBERLAND

Sixteenth to Nineteenth Centuries

The National Archives. See page 13 for coroners' records in King's Bench, Assizes and Chancery.

Cumbria Record Office, *Carlisle.*
North Cumberland [T/CR2]. Abstract books 1835-64.
Inquest books, incl. deposition notes, 1836-77 (incomplete).
Certificates of expenses 1861-63, 1867-72.

Cumbria Record Office, *Whitehaven.*
Liberties of Cockermouth and Egremont. (There were coroners here from 1292; the two offices were united from the 17th century to 1875. Some inquests are for places outside the liberties (as far as Upper Denton) when the estate coroner acted for the county coroner. Parts were transferred to the jurisdiction of the county coroner on the incorporation of Workington, 1888, and Whitehaven, 1894; the right to appoint was conveyed to the county council in 1910.
Inquests (indexed) 1610-1875.
Draft petitions or abstracts 1752-1857.
Expenses forms (vouchers) 1858-64.
[All above, D/Lec/CR1.]

Modern
(asterisked dates usually subject to 75-year closure)

Cumbria Record Office, *Carlisle.*
East Cumberland [T/CR1]. Abstracts of inquests 1877-1954*.
Papers, non-inquest cases, inquests, correspondence 1921-53*, 1956*-61*.
City of Carlisle Inquests 1873-2002, index on-going.

Cumbria Record Office, *Whitehaven.*
West Cumberland [YTCR3]. Quarterly abstracts of inquests 1907-43*.
Papers, incl. police reports, etc, 1956*-69*.
Coroners' notes 1959*-70*.
West Cumbria papers to 1979* [YTCR 3].
Honour of Cockermouth and Lordship of Millom [T/CR3]. Quarterly abstrs of inquests 1921*-29*.

DERBYSHIRE

A few hamlets in south Derbyshire were in part of the borough of Burton on Trent, Staffs., which had its own coroner.

Published

J.C. Cox, *Three Centuries of Derbyshire Annals*, **1** (1890), for a history of the various jurisdictions of coroners in the county, including the Honour of Tutbury, with some selections from the records.

Medieval

The National Archives [class JUST/2].

County. Rolls 17-20 Ed III [25], 22-26, 45 Ed III - 1 Ric II [26], 37-43 Ed III [268], 42-45 Ed III [28], 48-51 Ed III - 1 Ric II [29], 13-14 Ric II [30,m.6], 5-15 Ric II [31], 15-17 Ric II [32], 15-16 Ric II [255/14] (1343-93).

Derby Borough (right to coroner in 1256 charter). Rolls 35-41 Ed III [27], 2-13 Ric II [30,mm.1-5] (1361-90).

Sixteenth to Nineteenth Centuries

The National Archives. See page 13 for coroners' records in King's Bench, Assizes and Chancery.

Derbyshire Record Office*, Matlock, Derbyshire.*

County. Expenses claims (incl. date, place, name, cause of death, verdict) 1754-1869 [Q/AF8/1-12]. Indexed (see right).

Honour of Tutbury (covers a substantial part of Derbys. and Staffs. and certain parts of Leics. Notts. and Warws.). Inquest papers (incl. warrants, lists of jurors and witnesses, verdicts) 1665-1700 (at present unavailable).

Expenses claims 1761-1869 [Q/AF8/30-40].

Appletree Hundred. Expenses claims 1832-69 [Q/AF8/13-15].

Repton and Gresley Hundred (joint with Appletree Hundred 1858-69). Expenses claims 1832-69 [Q/AF8/16-19].

Scarsdale Hundred. Expenses claims 1759-1869 [Q/AF8/20-29].

Nottinghamshire Archives*, Nottingham.*

Barlborough. Copy of verdict 1669 [DDP 41/3].

Chesterfield, Scarsdale and Dunham. Power to appoint coroner 1631 [DDP 59/18].

Appointment *c.*1670 [DDP 19/2].

Scarsdale Hundred. Query re verdict 1680 [DDP 59/22].

Inquests (incl. verdicts, inventories of goods, mins of evidence, some giving causes of death and value of deodand) 1680-1769 [DDP 65/1-68].

Tibshelf. Summons to juryman 1860 and report of inquests 1872 [DD 354/93-4].

John Rylands Library, University of Manchester.

Honour of Tutbury. Appointments 1753, 1760, 1764, 1825.

Miscellaneous papers, incl. insignia 1830-32, and sale of the office of coroner [Bagshawe MSS]

Modern

(asterisked dates usually subject to 75-year closure)

Derbyshire Record Office*, Matlock.*

No modern records have been placed on permament deposit, but the repository stores depositions from a number of coroners from Derby and South Derbyshire, 1962*-78*.

Index to Derbyshire Inquests (Coroners' Bills) 1752-1869, at Derbys. R.O. (by Joan Measham, 81 Cavendish Road, Matlock, Derbys. DE4 3HD).

DEVON

Medieval

Published

R.F. Hunnisett, 'An early coroner's roll' (1229), *Bulletin of the Institute of Historical Research* **30** [for JUST 2/259].

The National Archives [class JUST/2].

County. Rolls 13 Hen III [259] (1229), 7-8 Ed I [269] (1278-80).

Sixteenth to Nineteenth Centuries

The National Archives. See page 13 for coroners' records in King's Bench, Assizes and Chancery.

Modern

(asterisked dates usually subject to 75-year closure)

Devon Record Office*, Exeter.*

Records neither catalogued nor indexed. Some relate to Exeter in the 19th and early 20th centuries, but most are post-1950*.

Plymouth & West Devon Record Office*, Plymouth. See leaflet, also on-line.*

Plymouth Borough. Inquisitions 1892-94, 1896-97 incomplete; 1896-97, incomplete 1910-26*, almost complete 1940*-45* [all acc. 1650]; 1947*-60* [1713/14-44]; 1960*-74* [2169/28-72]; 1974*-81* [various acc.'s].

Notice to remove a body out of England 1940* [1650].

Warrants to summon juries 1917-18 [1650/17-18].

Notes of post-mortem examinations (no inquisition) 1941*-45* [1651/41-45].

Counterfoils of death certs. 1941*-45* [1650]; 1946*-62* [1713/45-52].

Names of inquest files 1981* [1778/15].

Receipt for movement of body 19 Apr 1982* [1778/16].

Daily record books 1942*-43, 1947-67* [2169/1-9], 1968*-1988* [1711], 1997-2004*.

Post-mortem reports 1960*-73* [2169/10-27].

Post-mortem certificates etc 1934* [1713/1]; 1946*-1959* [1713/2-13].

Correspondence 1963*-73* [2169/73-74].

Accounts 1920-24* [1650].

Expenses 1933*-59* [2169/75].

Police maps of accidents 1960*-72* [2169/76].

Devon *(Modern)* continued

Plymouth & West Devon Record Office continued
Photographs 1960*-69* [2169/77-82].
Counterfoils of orders for burials 1944* [1650]; 1946*-58* [1713/53-54].
Counterfoils of orders for cremations, 1945*-59* [1713/55-57].
Counterfoils of orders for removal of bodies 1941*-58* [1713/58].
Fatal accident files 1957*-61* [1713/59].
Fatal accident photographs 1947*-64* and undated [1713/60-68].
West Devon (Bideford). Reports 1969* [1779/1-4]; 1972* [1779/6-9]; 1976*-77* [1779/12-15, 17-20].
Correspondence 1969* [1779/5]; 1972* [1779/10]; 1976*-77* [1779/16,21].
File on treasure trove, Broadwoodwidger 1973* [1779/11].

North Devon Record Office, *Barnstaple.*
North and West Devon District. Reports, daily record sheets and inquest files 1944-90 [1983].

DORSET

Sixteenth to Nineteenth Centuries

The National Archives. See page 13 for coroners' records in King's Bench, Assizes and Chancery.

Dorset History Centre, *Dorchester.*
County. Inquisitions 1698-1738 [D/FIL:X8,9], 1751-1771 [D.1/KK 11-18].
Badbury Hundred. Inquisition papers 1680-1842 [D/BKL: CF 1/3].
Cogdean Hundred. Inquisitions 1804-38 [D/WIM:JO 1336-1447].
Sherborne and Yetminster Hundred. Inquisitions 1883-1910 [C5].
Lyme Regis Borough. Inquisitions 1723-1836 [DC/LR: C1/1].
Poole. Inquests 1589-1884 (155) [CI 1589-1884].
Purbeck Inquisition 1760 (one only) [D/FIL: X10].
Sherborne Borough. Five inquisitions 1740-54 [D/SMC: KG 141-5].
Wareham and Purbeck Borough. Register of inquisitions 1867-82 [C2].

Modern
(asterisked dates usually subject to 75-year closure)

Dorset History Centre, *Dorchester.*
Eastern Division. Inquisitions, returns 1928*-93* [C3].
Southern Divison. Inquisitions and papers 1949*-52*, 1966*-68* [C1].
Western Division Inquisitions 1953*-93* [C6].
Bournemouth Borough. Inquisitions 1914*, 1934*-74* [C4].
Record books 1936*-74*.
Poole Borough. Inquisitions 1928*-72* [C5].

County DURHAM

From the earliest times, the coroners in County Durham (one for each of the four wards) were employees of the Prince Bishop and had additional duties as rent collectors (major tenants only) - hence the 'accounts' surviving from the middle ages.

Medieval

Durham University Library
Archives and Special Collections, *Durham.*

Church Commission Deposit.
Chester Ward. 38 accounts 1435-1549.
Darlington Ward. 14 accounts 1444-1542.
Easington Ward. 29 accounts 1443-1546.
Stockton Ward. 38 accounts 1413-1441.

Sixteenth to Nineteenth Centuries

The National Archives.
County. Inquisitions temp. James I (1603-25) [DURH 3/143].
Papers 1819-1828 [DURH 3/194].
See also page 13 for coroners' records in King's Bench, Assizes and Chancery.

Durham County Record Office, *Durham.*
Chester Ward. Diaries of inquests 1873-76, 1881-1882.
Verdicts of inquests 1881-93.
Case papers: inquests 1874-75, non-inquests 1873-1875.

Dean and Chapter Library, *Durham.*
Files of materials concerning 18th and 19th century coroners compiled by Ralph Nelson of Bondgate, Bishop Auckland (include coroners of Chester le Street, Darlington, Easington and Stockton).

Durham University Library
Archives and Special Collections, *Durham.*
Darlington and Stockton Wards. Inquests and related documents (incl. some lists of jurors) 1606-11 [Church Commission Miscellanea box 218 item 221689].

Modern
(asterisked dates usually subject to 75-year closure)

In 1907 Sunderland was created as a separate coroner's division. Chester Ward was subdivided in 1933; the five county jurisdictions were replaced in 1967 by North East, North West, East and South Districts; finally in 1974 the new county (after the creation of Tyne & Wear and Cleveland) had only two: North (incl. Chester le Street, Derwentside, Durham and Easington), and South (incl. Darlington, Sedgefield, Teesdale and Wear Valley).

Co. Durham *(Modern)* *continued*

Durham County Record Office, *Durham.*

Durham North. Registers of reported deaths 1974*-1983*, 1986*-94*.

Case papers: inquest and non-inquest 1974*-94* (sampled before 1993).

Durham South. Registers of reported deaths; case papers: inquest and non-inquest 1974*-1991* (sampled before 1986).

North-West District. Registers of reported deaths 1967*-74*.

Sampled case papers: inquest and non-inquest 1967*-74*.

South District. Registers of reported deaths 1967*-1974*.

Sampled case papers: inquest and non-inquest 1967*-73*.

Chester West Ward. Registers of reported deaths 1953*-67*.

Sampled case papers: inquest and non-inquest 1942*-67*.

Darlington Ward. Registers of reported deaths 1953*-67*.

Sampled case papers: inquests and non-inquests 1948*-64*.

Tyne & Wear Archives Service, *Newcastle upon Tyne.*

South Tyneside and Gateshead, incl. **North-East Durham, East Chester Ward.** Registers of deaths requiring coroner's involvement 1954*-94*.

Case files 1966*-93*.

Indexes of cases 1974*-93 [CR/ND].

Sunderland Borough. Registers of deaths reported 1953*-75*.

Daily record books 1952-77.

Inquest files 1962*-89* [T200, 523].

Index to inquests 1981*-90* [CR/SU].

ESSEX

Medieval

Published

C. Gross (1896) [for JUST 2/35(pt)].

The National Archives [class JUST 2/].

County. Rolls 9-10 Ed I [JUST 267], 43-49 Ed III [33B], 44-49 Ed III [35,mm.11-19], 50 Ed III - 3 Ric II [33A,mm.1-2], 2-3 Ric II [33A,mm.3-4], 1-2 Ric II [33A,mm.5-6], 3-13 Ric II [33A,m.9], 6-13 Ric II [33A,mm.13-17] (1369-1390).

Colchester Borough. Rolls 42 Ed II - 2 Ric II [33A,mm.7-8], 4-12 Ric II [33A,mm.10-12] (1368-89).

Dean and Chapter Library, Canterbury.

County. Roll 13 Ed II [MS Scrapbook A no.93] (1319-20) (described in Hist. MSS Comm. 5th report, Appx. p.462).

Essex continued

Sixteenth to Nineteenth Centuries

Published

J.S. Cockburn, *Calendar of Assize Records: Essex Indictments*, 1558-1625 (1979, 1982) [for ASSI 35, see pages 12-13].

The National Archives.

Duchy of Lancaster. Inquests and returns, with names of jurymen 1821-22 and a printed list of places in Essex which came within the jurisdiction of the coroner of the Duchy [DL 46/22].

See also page 13 for coroners' records in King's Bench (see below), Assizes [ASSI 35] and Chancery.

Essex Record Office, *Chelmsford.*

County. Bills for inquests, and vouchers (incl. fees, expenses, names of deceased, cause of death, verdict) 1752-1889 [Q/FAb].

A few inquisitions from 1587 on [Q/SR].

Inquests 1832-39 [Q/CR6/2].

TS calendar of King's Bench indictments 1558-1625 (originals in PRO).

Peculiar of Writtle and Roxwell. Papers re inquisitions, incl. verdicts, 1595, 1664-1702 [D/DP M607/1-11], 1814-41 [D/DP M608/1-17].

Verdicts and depositions 1801-36 [Cr/W1].

Bill for holding inquest Sep 1837 [D/DP E70].

Peculiar of the Sokens (Kirby, Thorpe and Walton). Verdicts and depositions 1758-73 [Cr/S1].

Papers re reimbursement of fees, incl. four inquisitions and depositions 1837-41 [Q/AX2].

Liberties of Duchy of Lancaster. Inquisitions 1822-24 [Q/AX 3/3].

Colchester Borough. Inquests among QS papers, 1774-83, 1797-1802, 1805-07.

Borough of Maldon. Inquests 1621-24 [D/B/3/3/210], 1746-68 [D/B 3/3/79].

Orders from coroners to serjeants at mace to summon jury 1635 [D/B 3/3/422/8].

Inquest papers on Richard Gilbert 1642 [D/B 3/3/465/1-3].

Record of inquest 1618 [D/B 3/3/479/3].

Modern

(asterisked dates usually subject to 75-year closure)

Places transferred to the newly-created County of London in 1888 will be found from that date under 'London'. Places incorporated into Greater London in 1965 remain under their former counties.

Essex Record Office, *Chelmsford.*

Colchester Borough. Inquests held, 1955*-71*.

Inquests and inquisitions 1953*-74*.

Southend Borough. Inquests and inquisitions 1960*-80*.

Registers 1960*-68*.

Daily record books 1959*-64*.

GLOUCESTERSHIRE and BRISTOL

Medieval

Published
C. Gross (1896) [for JUST 2/42; 45,m.2 (pt)] (1392-99).

The National Archives [class JUST 2/].
County. Rolls 26-37 Ed III [34,mm.18-28], 30-36 Ed III [34,mm.12-14], 33-37 Ed III [34,mm.8-11], 35-37 Ed III [34,mm.6-7], 41-49 Ed III [37,mm.488], 44-50 Ed III [37,mm.1-3], 44 Ed III - 2 Ric II [35,mm.9-10], 45-48 Ed III [35,mm.1-6], 49 Ed III - 2 Ric II [36,mm.1-4], 2 Ric II [255/10], 1-6 Ric II [38,m.6], 2-11 Ric II [38,mm.5,14-17], 7-9 Ric II [39,m.1], 8-11 Ric II [38,mm.12.13], 11-15 Ric II [39,mm.2-4], 13-15 Ric II [41], 16 Ric II [42], 16-21 Ric II [43], 17-21 Ric II [44], 19-21 Ric II [45,m.2], 21 Ric II [45,m.3] (1352-99).
Bristol Borough (right to coroner in 1256 charter). Roll 27-37 Ed III [34,mm.1-5] (1353-64).
Gloucester Borough. Rolls 27-30 Ed III [34,m.15]; 20,22,26,33-36 Ed III [34,mm.16-17], 42-44 Ed III [35,m.7], 45 Ed III - 2 Ric II [36,m.5], 47 Ed III - 1 Ric II [35,m.8], 7 Ric II [38,m.7], 8-11 [38,mm.8-11], 11-18 Ric II [40], 19-21 Ric II [45,m.1] (1353-98).

Sixteenth to Nineteenth Centuries

County coroners were given specific districts in 1844. From then until 1966 there were four, plus one each for Gloucester City and Tewkesbury Borough.

Published
W.P. Pitt, 'The coroners of Bristol', *Bristol & Glos. Arch. Soc.*, **55**, 135-41. C.17-19.
G.H.H. Glasgow, 'The election of Gloucestershire County coroners 1800-1888. *Gloucestershire History*, **13**.

The National Archives. See page 13 for coroners' records in King's Bench, Assizes and Chancery.

Gloucestershire Record Office, *Gloucester.*
County. Pre-1844:
Berkeley. Register of inquests 1790-1823 [D260].
Gloucester. Inquisitions 1797-1818 [D1406].
County. 1844-1966.
Forest of Dean. Registers of inquests 1868-71. Minutes of inquests 1868-1942* [both CO4].
Lower Division. Inquest files 1855-74 [CO1]. Calendared
Stroud Divison. Inquest files 1857-1966*. Registers of deaths 1831-48, 1881-1913 [both CO3]. 19th century calendar in progress.
Gloucester Borough. Inquisitions 1642-60 [GBR G2].
Tewkesbury Borough. Inquest files 1733-91 [TBR].

Bristol Record Office, *Bristol.*
Bristol. Inquisitions [in QS records] 1743, 1756-1758, 1776-77, 1779-89, 1791-1801, 1805-06, 1809-13, 1816-17, 1821-22, 1824-28 (all other coroners' records before 1936 are thought to have been destroyed).

Modern
(asterisked dates usually subject to 75-year closure)

See note above for jurisdictions from 1844. In 1966 county coroners were reduced to three, with changes of areas in 1974 (when the county of Avon, encompassing Bristol, was created).

Gloucestershire Record Office, *Gloucester.*
County. 1844-1966:
Forest of Dean. Minutes of inquests 1868-1942*. Inquest files 1960*-66* [both CO4]. Register of deaths 1960*-66* [CO9].
Lower Division. Inquest files 1923, 1931*, 1946*-1966* [CO1].
Stroud Divison. Inquest files 1857-1966*. Registers of deaths 1881-1913 [both CO3].
Upper Division. Inquest files 1936*-66* (calendar in progress). Registers of deaths 1926*-36*, 1953*-64*. Daily record books 1917*-31*, 1936*-61*, 1961-65 [CO7]. Correspondence 1936*-54* [all CO2].
County 1966-1974:
Cotswold Divison. Inquest files 1966*-74* [CO7]. Daily record book 1966*-76 [CO7]
Lower Division. Inquest files 1966*-72* [CO8].
West Gloucestershire Divison. Inquest files 1966*-74* [CO9]. Register of deaths 1966*-71* [CO9]
County. 1974 on:
Cheltenham Division. Inquest files 1974*-76* [CO7]. Case papers 1977-92 Register of deaths reported 1977-83 Daily record book 1977-81 [all CO7]
Cotswold Division Register of deaths reported 1974*-76* [CO7]
Gloucester Division. Inquest files 1974*-82* [CO10]. Files 1990*-91* [CO10]
Gloucester Borough. Inquest files 1921*-74*. Forms 100 1953*-74*. Correspondence 1953*-62*. Registers of deaths 1944*-74* [all CO 6], 1971-81 [CO10].
Tewkesbury Borough. Inquest files 1890-1936*, 1951*-65* [CO5].

Bristol Record Office.
See note above re destruction of pre-1936 records.
Bristol. Inquisitions with some associated papers 1936*-67*.
Post mortem reports 1951*-92* (incomplete).
Inquests 1968*-92* (almost complete).
Single cases: explosion 1951*, prison death 1956*, hospital enquiry 1969*.
Jury books 1951*-66*.
Disbursements (sample only) 1974*.
Registers of deaths reported 1954*-75*, previously held by this repository, have been returned to the coroner.

HAMPSHIRE

Medieval

The National Archives [class JUST 2/].

County. Rolls 1-2 Ed I [262, 278], 24-25 Ed III [152], 37-44 Ed III [153], 40-45 Ed III [154,m.3], 1-16 Ric II [155], 12-14 Ric II [JUST 1/197] (1272-74, 1350-93).

Isle of Wight. Roll 1-16 Ric II [156] (1377-93).

Southampton Borough. Roll 40-44 Ed III [154,m.1] (1366-71).

Winchester City. 40-44 Ed III [154,m.2], 2-4 Ric II [157,m.6], 4-5 Ric II [157,m.5], 6 Ric II [157,m.1], 7-8 Ric II [157,m.2], 12 Ric II [157,m.3]; 13,15 Ric II [157,m.4] (1366-92).

Sixteenth to Nineteenth Centuries

The National Archives.

Inquests on convicts at Spithead and Portsmouth Harbour, 1816-1832 [HCA1/102-109].

See also page 13 for coroners' records in King's Bench, Assizes and Chancery.

Hampshire Record Office, *Winchester.*

County. Petition for new appointment 1798 [1M41].

Hundred of Christchurch and Liberty of Westover. Inquisitions, depositions 1841-51 [P'copy 288/88-196].

Winchester City. Single inquisitions, 1618, 1624 (2), 1651, 1680 with jury list, 1688, 1698 [W/S5/1-3, W/D3/66,79,88, A1758 Feverell].

Certificates of deodands forfeited at inquest, 1838 [W/D3/247].

Andover Borough. Single inquisitions and orders, 1703, 1706 and n.d. [2/CN/1-3].

Southampton Archives Services.

Southampton Borough. Appointments and bills [in Borough Minute Books] from 1835 (indexed from 1895; index 1835-94 in progress).

It is believed that all early coroners' records relating to **Portsmouth** were lost during the war.

Isle of Wight: see above right.

Modern
(asterisked dates usually subject to 75-year closure)

Hampshire Record Office, *Winchester.*

Hundred of Fordingbridge.
Inquisitions, depositions, etc, 1955*-64* [133M82].

Central Hampshire (incl. **Winchester** from 1974). Inquisitions, depositions, etc, 1941*-79* [11M70].

Western Hampshire. Inquisitions, depositions, etc, 1956*-73* [133M82].

Test Valley and Borough of Eastleigh. Inquisitions, depositions, etc. 1974*-79* [137,83].

Winchester City. Inquisitions, depositions, etc, 1936*-1974* [W/D5]; see also Central Hampshire above.

Southampton Archives Services.

City of Southampton. Inquest files 1936*-76*.
Non-inquest files (post mortem cases) 1960*-76*.
Appointments and bills: see above.

Isle of Wight County Record Office, *Newport.*

Isle of Wight. All inquests, with and without post-mortem, from 1956*.
Register 1850-64, 1866-1906 (indexed).
(Registers since 1934 are retained by the coroner.)

HEREFORDSHIRE
(see also Worcestershire)

Sixteenth to Nineteenth Centuries

The National Archives. See page 13 for coroners' records in King's Bench, Assizes and Chancery.

Herefordshire Record Office, *Hereford.*

Hereford area. Inquests 1825-26 [Pateshall papers, indexed].

Leominster District. Treasure trove 1892-4 (1 case).

Modern
(asterisked dates usually subject to 75-year closure)

Herefordshire Record Office, *Hereford.*

Hereford City. Inquests 1952*-81*.

Leominster District. Inquests 1936*-74*.

HERTFORDSHIRE

Medieval

The National Archives.

County. Roll 13-14 Ed I [JUST 2/260] (1284-86).

Sixteenth to Nineteenth Centuries

Published

J.S. Cockburn, *Calendar of Assize Records: Hertfordshire Indictments*, 1558-1625 (2 vols., 1975) [for ASSI 35, see pages 12-13].

The National Archives. See page 13 for coroners' records in King's Bench, Assizes and Chancery.

Hertfordshire Archives & Local Studies, *Hertford.*
Note. Coroners' records are not yet fully catalogued.

Hemel Hempstead. Returns on inquests 1890-1901.
Miscellaneous papers 1887-94.

Hertford. Inquest book 1827-40.
Inquest papers 1870-83.

Modern
(asterisked dates usually subject to 75-year closure)

Hertfordshire Archives & Local Studies, *Hertford* (see note above).

Bishop's Stortford. Case papers 1953*-58*.

Hemel Hempstead. Case papers 1908-59* (incomplete).

Hertford. Inquest papers 1904, 1912.
Case papers 1934*-94* (indexed).

Hitchin. Case papers 1960*-95*.

St Albans. Case papers 1942*-91*.

Watford. Registers 1964*-74*.
Case papers 1944*-74*.

HUNTINGDONSHIRE

See also Northamptonshire.

Medieval

***Huntingdonshire Archives**, Huntingdon.*
Godmanchester Borough. Roll 1294-1302 [1/4,13].

Sixteenth to Nineteenth Centuries

The National Archives. See page 13 for coroners' records in King's Bench, Assizes and Chancery.

***Huntingdonshire Archives**, Huntingdon.*
Norman Cross. Appointments 1806, 1867, 1884 [Coroner 1b/1906/1/1].
Various Hundreds. Appointments 1869-1932* [HCP15/1697/1/1-17; HCP15/1696/1-4; Coroner 1b/1906/1/1].
Godmanchester Borough. Inquests, informations, 1557-1633, 1823-32 [2/12-13, 17].
Huntingdon Borough. Inquests 1818-23 [5/5].

Modern
(asterisked dates usually subject to 75-year closure)

***Huntingdonshire Archives**, Huntingdon.*
Huntingdon District. Inquests without jury 1940*-1941* [Coroner 1a/268/10-11].
Inquests with depositions 1952*-59*, 1960*-72*, 1973-79* [Coroner 3-5/1838; 10-28/2534; 30-42/2904].
Depositions in Pink Form B (sudden death files) 1952*-54*, 1956*-60*, 1960*-72*, 1972*; 1977*-1979* [Coroner 1d-2/1838; 6-9/2534; 29/2534; 44-5/2904].
Miscellaneous correspondence (some incl. depositions) 1952*-56*, 1965*-74* [Coroner 2/1838; 46/2904].
Returns and extracts from statistics 1865-1912, 1917*-40's*.
Counterfoils of: orders for burials 1911-36*; certificates of findings of jury after inquest 1912-1941*, 1951*-64*; notifications to Registrar that inquests unnecessary 1913*-40*, 1951*-63*.
Returns of deaths due to railway accidents 1913*-1925*.
Certificates for cremation after inquest 1934*, 1951*-64*.
Acknowledgment of receipts of notices to remove bodies 1931*.
Death registers 1953*-76* [Coroner 43/2904].
Liberty of Ramsey. Inquests 1899, 1901-04, 1906-1911 [Coroner SS78/2513].
Norman Cross. Inquests 1914*-25*, 1932*-42*, 1944*-47* [Coroner 1b/1906/1/2a-e].
Miscellaneous depositions and correspondence 1918*-43* [Coroner 1c/1906/2/3].
Book of receipts and expenses for inquests 1889-1916* [Coroner 1c/1906/2/14].
Hurstingstone. Appointment 1924* [Coroner 1b/1906/1/1].
Various Hundreds. Appointments: see above.

KENT

Medieval

Published
R.F. Hunnisett, 'A coroner's roll of the Liberty of Wye 1299-1314', in R.F. Hunnisett and J.B. Post (eds.), *Medieval Legal Records* (1978) [for JUST 2/276].

The National Archives [class JUST 2/].
County. Roll 7 Ed II - 11 Ed III (estreats) [47] (1313-1338).
Liberty of Wye. Roll 27 Ed I - 7 Ed II [276] (1299-1314).

Canterbury Cathedral and City Archives.
Canterbury. Coroner's roll 1337-38 [CC/C5/C/1]

Sixteenth to Nineteenth Centuries

Published
J.S. Cockburn, *Calendar of Assize Records: Kent Indictments*, 1558-1675 (1979, 1980, 1989, 1995), 1676-1688 (in press, P.R.O., 1997) [for ASSI 35, see pages 12-13].
L.A. Knafla, *Kent at Law 1602*, vol. 1 (1994). Contains all Assizes and Quarter Sessions cases for that year.

The National Archives. See page 13 for coroners' records in King's Bench, Assizes and Chancery.

***Centre for Kentish Studies,** Maidstone.*
Dover. 1880-1916.
Maidstone. Accounts 1836-1902.
Records sampled on unknown criteria:
East Kent. Volumes 1887-1932*
Maidstone. Papers 1857-60.
Tonbridge. Papers 1894-1902.
Cranbrook. Papers 1894.
There are also some records, unlisted, in borough collections, e.g. Dover and Maidstone. Historical Manuscripts Commission lists coroner's papers 1713-17 [Radnor 4712(04)], 1829-1923* for **Romney** and **Lydd** [D G Ward 5301: 037/4,044], and Dover 1836-51 [15570(024)].

Canterbury Cathedral and City Archives.
Canterbury. Inquisitions, reports, case papers, 1562-1818, 1893-1967* (gaps) [CC/C5].
Inquests, inquiries 1881-1903; Acs 1886-1906. Daily record, register of inquests 1894-1910.
Note. Other records, and those up to 1942, are believed to have been sent for salvage during the war.

Modern
(asterisked dates usually subject to 75-year closure)

Places transferred to the newly created County of London in 1888 will be found from that date under 'London'. Places incorporated into Greater London in 1965 remain under their former counties.

***Centre for Kentish Studies,** Maidstone.*
Records of **Sittingbourne, Faversham, Dartford, Gillingham, Gravesend** and **Sheerness**, 1949*-1976*.

Kent ***(Modern)*** continued

East Kent 1955*-68*.
Dover 1880-1916, 1931*-78*.
Folkestone 1901-74*.
Records sampled on unknown criteria:
East Kent. Vols. 1887-1932*; papers 1918-79*.
South Kent 1932*-52*, 1961*-74* papers, 1954*-1971* registers.
West Kent. Papers 1932*-36*.
Maidstone. Volumes 1895-1953*.
Papers 1937*-45*.
Tonbridge. Papers 1928*-47*.

Canterbury Cathedral and City Archives
See note left.

LANCASHIRE

Sixteenth to Nineteenth Centuries

The National Archives.
Palatinate of Lancashire. Inquisitions 1626-1832 [PL 26/285-295].

Lancashire Record Office, *Preston.*
See Information Leaflet 10, also on-line.
County. Quarter Sessions Petitions include accounts submitted by the County Coroners which give brief details of inquests held.
Manor of Walton-le-Dale. Inquests, etc, 1627-1824.
Clitheroe Borough. Inquests 1795, 1801 and n.d.
Juror's oath and witnesses' depositions 1815.
Uncatalogued collections, not normally available without prior arrangement:
Manor of Hale. Inquests 1711-12, 1716, 1721, 1723, 1742-43, 1752, 1757, 1761, 1769, 1772, 1774, 1778-79, 1787, 1793, 1799.
Manor of Prescot. Inquests 1847-59.

Manchester Central Library Local Studies Unit.
Manchester. Depositions 1851-52 [M381/1/1/1,2].

Liverpool City Library (Record Office & Local History Department), *Liverpool.*
Liverpool. Register of inquests 1852-65.
Liverpool. Inquest registers 1898-1915.
Computerised index (not available).

Wigan Heritage Service, *Wigan.*
Wigan Borough. Inquisitions post mortem 1804-11.
Inquest books 1836-40 (both calendared).

Modern
(asterisked dates usually subject to 75-year closure)

Cumbria Record Office, *Barrow-in-Furness.*
Barrow, Furness.
Reports 1944*-93*.
Counterfoils: non-inquests 1933*-79*.
Order for burial 1926*-79*.
Cert E for cremation 1941*-79*.
Removal of body from England 1939*-61*.
Cert after inquest 1938*-83*.
Home Office returns 1944-77 (except 1970).

Lancashire ***(Modern)*** continued

Lancashire Record Office, *Preston.*
Lancaster District. Inquests, police reports, notices of death from the County Asylum and the Royal Albert Asylum, Lancaster, *c.*1898-1934* [uncatalogued, and being sampled; prior arrangement to view necessary].
Preston District. Daily records 1958*-94*.
Log books 1949*-93*.
Inquest files 1950*-81* (sampled).
Enquiry files 1972*-74*.
Blackburn District. Registers of deaths 1950*-94*.
Inquest files 1919 (complete), 1950*-81* (sampled).
Enquiry files 1972*-74*.
Depositions 1919*.
Blackpool Borough Inquest files c1955*-74* (to be sampled).
Salford District. Daily records 1935*-71*.
Index books 1962*-69*.
Telephone message books 1960*-69*.
Inquest files 1926; 1928; 1935*-70 (sampled).
Rochdale District. Daily records 1911-42*.
Inquest files 1933*-37* (to be sampled).
West Derby District. Registers of deaths 1882-1971*.
Dispensing registers 1952*-67*
Inquest files 1957*-74* (sampled)
Special files 1945*-64*.
Treasure trove files 1913-53.
Scrap books 1925-54.
Bury District. Daily records 1937*-71*.
Registers of inquests 1912-71*.
Registers of enquiries 1904-71*.
Inquest files 1918*-71* (sampled).
Plans 1934*-50*.
Accounts 1963-71.
Telephone message book 1950*.
Lancaster Inquest files c1898-1934* (to be sampled).

County districts post-1974:
Preston and South-West Lancashire. Daily records 1974*-82*.
Log Books 1974*-80*.
Inquest files 1974*-84* (to be sampled).
Enquiry files 1974*-84* (to be destroyed after 15 years).
Blackburn, Hyndburn and Ribble Valley.
Registers of deaths 1975*-94*.
Inquest files 1975*-81* (to be sampled).
Blackpool. Inquest files 1977*-82*.
Burnley, Pendle and Rossendale. Registers of deaths 1971*-93*.
Daily record books 1969*-92*.
Inquest files 1978*-80*.
North Lancashire Inquest files 1979*-80*.
Preston and South West Lancashire.
Daily record books 1974*-94*.
Log books 1974*-93*.
Inquest files 1974*-84*.
Annual summaries of deaths reported 1989-93.

Liverpool City Library (Record Office), *Liverpool.*
Bootle (S.W. Lancashire).
Coroners' Officer papers.
Index to deaths reported 1949*-66*.
Deaths reported 1967*-69* [COR/L/14/1-4].
Liverpool. Court diaries and indexes 1924*-78* [COR/L/6/1-2].
Indexes to deaths reported 1970*-78* [COR/L/9/1-9
List of deaths reported 1967*-68*.
Receipts, copied depositions 1911-50* [COR/L/12].
Inquests, presumptions of death: World War Two: 1941*.
Presumptions of death, war operations (indexed): 1941*-43* [COR/L/7/1-3].
Newspaper cuttings 1892-1928, 1971-74, 1978 [COR/L/10/1-10].
Coroners' Society reports 1890-1923, 1938-54 [COR/L/11/1-7].
Receipt books 1975*-78*.
Non-inquest registers 1893-1953* [COR/L/3/1-6].
Inquest papers 1938*-79* [COR/L/8].
Passing post-mortems 1939*-41*, 1969*-79*.
Index to inquest book 1915*-76 [COR/L/2/1-4]*.
Index to non-inquest regs. 1915*-27* [COR/L/4].
Index to passing casebook 1914*-53* COR/L/5].
Register of inquests 1898-1970* COR/L/1/1-20].
Non-inquest book 1915*-29*.
Papers relating to Henderson's fire, 1960* [COR/L/1/13/1-5]: depositions, transcripts of evidence, inquest proceedings, photographs, inspector's reports, newspaper cuttings.
Southport. Inquest 1974*-81*.
Dispensations 1974*-82*.
Passing post-mortems 1975*-84*.
Police passing post-mortem forms 1980*.
Police reports on sudden deaths 1977*-78*. Police reports 1978*-79*.Police photographs 1973*-76*.

Oldham Cultural and Information Services.
Oldham: Inquisitions 1905, 1915 (incomplete) [32/1-2].
Inquisitions and (except 1927 and 1935-36) notices of death 1916-37* [32/3-19].

Greater Manchester Record Office (documents will be made available only in the coroner's office).
Bolton. Inquests 1961*-81*.
Bury. Inquests, post mortems 1971*-73*.
Manchester. Inquests, post-mortems 1959-2005*; indexes 1918-2005.
Oldham. Inquests, post-mortems 1955*-69*.
Rochdale. Inquests, post mortems 1961*-91*, index.
Salford Borough. Inquests etc 1912-25, 1932-35, 1937-74*. *Information leaflet on-line.*

Manchester Central Library Local Studies Unit.
Manchester. Newspaper cuttings 1900-38 [M38/12]; Depositions 18511-85 [Archives Unit].

Wigan Heritage Service, *Wigan.*
Wigan. Inquest books 1917-19.
Registers of deaths reported 1952*-74*.
Inquest expenses books 1912-27*, 1945*-74*.
Deposition papers 1948*-74*.
Post mortem reports 1949*-53*, 1959*-64*.

LEICESTERSHIRE

See also Derbyshire: Honour of Tutbury.

Medieval

Published
M. Bateson (ed.), *Records of the Borough of Leicester*, **1** (1899) and 2 (1901) [for BR IV/6/1-2].
Trans. Leics. Arch. Soc. **21** [for JUST 2 57(pt), 61(pt)].

The National Archives [class JUST 2/].
County. Rolls 35-36 Ed III [48], 36-39 Ed III [49], 38-42 Ed III [51], 39-41 Ed III [52], 40-46 Ed III [54], 42-49 Ed III [55], 43-45 Ed III [56], 49 Ed III - 3 Ric II, 13-17 Ric II [57] (pubd.), 51 Ed III - 7 Ric II [58,mm.1-12], 2-12, 17 Ric II [59], 17 Ric II - 7 Hen IV [60,mm.1-9], 17 Ric II - 14 Hen IV [61] (pt pubd.), 7 Hen IV - 2 Hen V [63], 1 Hen V [62,m.1] (1361-1415).
Leicester Borough. 36-39 Ed III [50], 39-43 Ed III [53,m.1], 43-51 Ed III [53,mm.2-5], 1-8 Ric II [58,m.14], 8-14 Ric II [58,m.13], 17-19 Ric II [60,m.13], 17-19 Ric II [60,m.13], 21 Ric II - 7 Hen IV [60,mm.10-12], 8 Hen IV - 1 Hen V [62,m.2]. (1362-1414).

The Record Office for Leicestershire, Leicester and Rutland, *Wigston Magna.*
Leicester Borough. Coroners' rolls 1297-1327 [BR IV/6/1-2] (published).

Sixteenth to Nineteenth Centuries

The National Archives. See page 13 for coroners' records in King's Bench, Assizes and Chancery.

The Record Office for Leicestershire...
Leicestershire District. Inquests 1869-73 [CO1/1-17] (earlier inquests have been destroyed).
Quarter Sessions records: papers re. division of county into coroners' districts 1873-73 [QS40/1/1]
Fees and salaries 1821-1939* [QS 40/2/1-3].
Inquisitions into compulsory purchase of land re Midland Counties Railway 1838-39 [QS 82/3/1-4].
Appointments of deputies 1844-75 [QS 87/1-6].
Papers re. election of coroners for North and South Leics. districts 1873 [109'30/23].

Modern
(asterisked dates usually subject to 75-year closure)

The Record Office for Leicestershire...
Leicester and South Leicestershire District.
Inquest papers 1891-1981* [CO1/18-87, DE2491, 3083, 3172, 3313].
North Leicestershire District.
Inquest papers 1969(-78* [DE3127, 3475, 4480].
Note that all earlier rercords have been destroyed.
Other records (all districts).
Appointments of deputies and assistants 1896-1958 [CC/8/1B/1-20].
Declarations of office 1901, 1924 [CC/8/1A/1-2].

LINCOLNSHIRE

Medieval

Published

R.F. Hunnisett, 'The reliability of inquisitions as historical evidence', in D.A. Bullough and R.L. Storey (eds.), *The Study of Medieval Records: Essays in honour of Kathleen Major* (1971) [for JUST 2/80 (pt), JUST 2/87 (pt)].

W.A. Morris, *The Early English County Court* (Univ. of California Publ. in History **14**) [for JUST 2/256/8-23 (pt), 2/83 (pt].

C.M. Woolgar, 'A Lincolnshire Coroner's Roll', *Lincolnshire History and Archaeology* **16** (1981) [for the roll (1290-1) found among the muniments of Magdalen College, Oxford].

The National Archives [class JUST 2/].

County. Rolls 7-10 Ed III [256/6-7], 3-4 Hen IV [274], 4-5 Hen IV [275] (1333-1404).

Holland. Rolls 16-17 Ed III [64,m.21], 17-19 Ed III [64,m.19-20], 19-22 Ed III [64,m.14], 25-43 Ed III [67.mm.7-32], 43-48 Ed III [74,mm.1-10], 47-49 Ed III [78], 50 Ed III - 4 Ric II [82], 4-7 Ric II [88], 15-19 Ric II [92] (1342-96).

Kesteven. Rolls 22-23 Ed III [64,mm.1-2], 23-30 Ed III [66], 30-42 Ed III [69], 42-44, 47-49 Ed III [72], 44-47 Ed III [74,mm.11-13], 50 Ed III - 6 Ric II [83], 7-19 Ric II [85,mm.8-15] (1348-96).

North Riding. Rolls 15-20 Ed III [64,m.18], 20-23 Ed III [64,m.13], 21-38 Ed III [67,mm.1-6], 38-42 Ed III [221], 44-49 Ed III [75], 49-50 Ed III, 5-14 Ric II [81], 1-5 Ric II [84], 14-19 Ric II [91,mm.5-6] (1341-96).

South Riding. Rolls 15-21 Ed III [64,mm.15-17], 17-28 Ed III [65], 18-23 Ed III [64,mm.5-8], 19-27 Ed III [256/8-23], 28-35 Ed III [67,mm.33-40], 35-49 Ed III [70], 4-10 Ric II [89], 13-19 Ric II [91,mm.1-4] (1341-1396).

West Riding. Rolls 21-23 Ed III [64,mm.11-12], 41-42 Ed III [64,mm.11-12], 41-42 Ed III [71], 43-45 Ed III [73], 45-49 Ed III [77], 3-6 Ric II [86], 6-19 Ric II [85,mm.3-7] (1347-96).

Liberty of Well Wapentake. Roll 17-22 Ed III [64,m.9] (1343-48).

Grimsby Borough. Rolls 30-37 Ed III [68,m.1], 37-47 Ed III [68.m.2], 37-47 Ed III [68.m.2], 48-49 Ed III [68,m.3], 49 Ed III - Ric II [79], 9-12 Ric II [90,m.1**], 13-14 Ric II [90,m.3], 16-19 Ric II [93,m.3] (1356-96).**

Lincoln City. Rolls 18-22 Ed III [64,m.10], 38-50 Ed III [67,mm.41-50], 49 Ed III - 12 Ric II [80], 5-6, 14-16 Ric II [85,m.2], 3-15 Ric II [87], 16-19 Ric II [93,mm.1-2,4-5] (1344-96).

Naveby Borough. Roll 17, 19 Ric II [91,m.7] (1393-1396).

Stamford Borough. Rolls 17-22 Ed III [64,mm.3-4], 44-49 Ed III [76], 1-8 Ric II [85,m.1], 9-18 Ric II [90,m.2] (1343-95).

Welton Borough. 14-19 Ric II [91,m.8].

Magdalen College, *Oxford.*

South Riding. Roll 18-19 Ed I [Estate Paper 83/41] (1290-91) (published).

North East Lincolnshire Archives, *Grimsby.*

County. Coroner's roll 1286/7 [1/521].

Sixteenth to Nineteenth Centuries

The National Archives. See page 13 for coroners' records in King's Bench, Assizes and Chancery.

British Library, *London.*

Coroners' records 1669-1701 [Add. MS 31028].

Lincolnshire Archives, *Lincoln.*

Lincolnshire. Inquests 1753-74 [INQ] Indexed.

Kirton (Lindsey). Registers of inquests 1837-80.
Fee book 1831-40.
Counterfoils 1875-80.
Inquisitions 1900.
Reports of Coroners' Society 1890-1901 [all ref. Lamb 4].
Inquests and depositions 1869-1911 [Lindsey County Council deposit].

Stamford and South Rutland. Inquests 1894-1909.

Modern

(asterisked dates usually subject to 75-year closure)

Lincolnshire Archives, *Lincoln.*

Boston. Inquests and depositions *c.*1910-83*.

Boston and Spalding. Inquests 1984-91.

Caistor. Inquests and reported deaths 1945-47.

Kirton (Lindsey). Inquests, depositions and pink form counterfoils 1942*-73*.

Lincoln City. Inquests, depositions, etc, 1911-30*, 1944*-73*.
Returns 1936*-71*.

Lincoln North District. A few depositions and case papers 1901-16*.
Inquests, depositions, reports, etc, 1965*-74*.

Louth. Inquests 1946*-71*.
Reports, depositions 1943*-62*.
Notebook 1944*-46*.

North Kesteven Registers of deaths reported 1952*-74*.
Inquests 1971-74.
Correspondence etc 1954*-74*.

Spalding. Inquests 1971*-83*
General files 1954*-83*

Spilsby. Inquests 1900-87* (some years missing).

West Kesteven. Inquests, depositions 1959*-74*.
Death registers 1954*-74*.

North East Lincolnshire Archives, *Grimsby.*

Scunthorpe District. Inquest files (incl. post-mortems) 1974*-82* [394]. The Scunthorpe District was then amalgamated into the North Humberside and Scunthorpe District.

Grimsby Borough. Registers of deaths 1953*-61*.

Daily record sheets, depositions, inquest reports, reports without inquest 1946*-63* [209].

LONDON

Before 1889, this section relates to the City of London and Borough of Southwark (technically in Surrey) only. From 1889 it covers the whole county of London as it was until 1965. Places incorporated into Greater London in 1965 will be found under their former counties.

Medieval

Published

W. Kellaway, 'The coroner in medieval London' in A.E.J. Hollaender and W. Kellaway (eds.), *Studies in London History, presented to Philip Edward Jones* (1969).

H.T. Riley (ed.), *Memorials of London and London Life in the 13th, 14th and 15th Centuries* (1868) for rolls in the Corporation of London Record Office.

R.R. Sharpe (ed.), *Calendar of Coroners' Rolls of the City of London 1300-1378* (1913) for abstracts of rolls in the C.L.R.O.

R.R. Sharpe, *Calendar of Letter Book B* (1900), incl. roll for 1276-78.

The National Archives.

City. Rolls 1 Ed I [JUST 2/279] (1272-3), 9-10 Ed II [JUST 2/94A] (1315-17).

Corporation of London R.O., *Guildhall, London. See Information Sheet 11, also on-line.*
See with London Metropolitan Archives

City. Rolls 1244, 1276 [Misc. rolls AA, BB], 1276-78 [Letter Book B], 1300-78 (gaps) [Coroners' Rolls A-I].

Sixteenth to Nineteenth Centuries

The City Corporation appointed its own coroner from 1483, and one for Southwark from 1550; in practice, this was often a joint appointment. The City coroner had additional jurisdictions over Holloway Prison, Middlesex, 1852-1965, and over non-fatal fires in London, 1888-1977.

The National Archives. See page 13 for coroners' records in King's Bench, Assizes and Chancery.

Corporation of London Records Office. See with *London Metropolitan Archives.*

City. 1590 [Coroners' Roll J].
Inquests and depositions (incl. Southwark) 1788-1837 (indexed).
Inquests 1838-1901 (indexed).
Fire inquests: orignal inquests (1888-98), duplicate inquests (1888-1912).
Writs and bills of costs 1805-29.
Cash accounts 1837-57.
Vouchers for disbursements (1885 part).

Southwark. Inquests and depositions 1788-1837 (under City, above); 1838-1901 (indexed).
Cash accounts 1837-57, 1859 (part).

Prisons, etc. Newgate 1800-39; Fleet 1800-39; Poultry Compter 1800-15; Bridewell Hospital 1800-38; Giltspur Street Compter 1800-29; Southwark Borough Compter 1818-38; Ludgate 1802-14; Whitecross St Compter 1815-1839 (for Holloway, see London main series).
Other prison inquests may be found in the main series of inquest records.

Modern
(asterisked dates usually subject to 75-year closure)

Corporation of London Records Office. See with *London Metropolitan Archives.*

City. Inquests 1901-19.
Depositions (later inquest cases) 1901-37*.
Reports on non-inquest cases 1901-37*.
Inquest (incl. depositions) and non-inquest cases 1941*-84* indexed.
Police deaths, 1911, 1913* (2 cases).
Fire inquests: duplicate inquests (1888-1912), depositions and inquests (1905-37* except 1918, 1923-25), officers' reports 1901-37*, 1940*-47*.
Fires 1897, 1902 (2), 1912.
Crypt of Guildhall 1977*.

Southwark. Inquests 1861-1901 (index); 1901-19*.
Depositions (later inquest cases) 1901-32*.
Reports on non-inquest cases 1901-32*.
Fire inquest reports 1901-15*, 1919*-22* (all L.C.C. districts).

London Metropolitan Archives
40 Northampton Road, London EC1R 0HB.

County. Inquests on victims of the steamship 'Princess Alice' 1878 [COR/PA/1-47] (see G. Thurston, *The Great Thames Disaster* (1965) and the *Registration Service Magazine*, **10** (1972)).

Southern District. Depositions (all 10% sample) 1932*-39*, 1943*-64*.
War casualty cases, 1941*-45*, and Lewisham rail disaster, 1957*.

Northern District. Depositions (all 10% sample) 1933*-65*, register (part) 1930* [COR/A/21].

Central District. Registers 1889-1930* [COR/A/7-13].
Depositions (10% sample) 1927*-32*.

Western District. Registers 1892 [COR/A/8], 1930*-32* [COR/A/21], 1938*-54* [COR/A/22 (Hammersmith only).
Depositions (10% sample) 1927*-65*.
Westminster Ct. 1944*-45.
Papers 1930*-32*.

Eastern District. Registers 1925*-34* [COR/A/23-24].
Home Office returns 1921*-35*.
Depositions (10% sample) 1927*-55*.

South Western District. depositions (10% sample) 1927*-28*, 1940*-43*.
War casualty cases 1941*-45*.

South Eastern District. Depositions (10% sample) 1927*-34*.

North Eastern District. Registers 1902-30* [COR/A/14-21].
Depositions (10% sample) 1927*-30* (incl. all non-inquest cases Jan-May 1927*).

MIDDLESEX

Before 1889, the section relates to the whole historic county except for the City of London itself. From 1889 those places transferred to the newly created County of London will be found under 'London' above. Places incorporated in Greater London in 1965 will be found under their former counties.

Medieval

Published

C. Gross (1896) [for JUST 2/95].

W.A. Morris, *The Early English County Court*, Univ. of California Publ. in History **14** [for JUST 2/256/29, incorrectly dated to Ed I].

The National Archives.

County [class JUST 2/]. Rolls 22-23 Ed III [94B], 39-40 Ed III [95, pubd.], 3-9 Ric II [96,mm.1-3,5-6], 10-13 Ric II [97A,mm.1,4], 11-12 Ric II [97B], 12-13 Ric II [97A,m.5], 13-14 Ric II [255/12], 14-17 Ric II [98,m.1], 15-17 Ric II [98,m.4], 16-19 Ric II [99,mm.1,3], 18-21 Ric II [100,mm.1-2], 22-23 Ric II [256/29, pubd.] (1348-99).

[class KB 9/] 1 Hen IV [184,mm.2-3]; 185/2,m.54], 2 Hen IV [185/1,mm.78-79], 2-3 Hen IV [191,mm.14-15], 3 Hen IV [187,m.17], 4 Hen IV [186,mm.49,52-54], 6 Hen IV [94,m.22], 6-7 Hen IV [990,m.12], 7-8 Hen IV [195,m.12], 9 Hen IV [195,m.37], 11 Hen IV [197,m.21], 1 Hen V [202,m.54], 3 Hen V [JUST 2/101], 2-3 Hen VI [220,m.19] (1399-1416).

12-13 Ed IV [KB 9/335,mm.40-41] (1472-74).

Liberty of the Abbot of Westminster [class JUST 2/]. Rolls 32-33 Ed III [255/7], 5-9 Ric II [96,m.4], 10-13 Ric II [97A,mm.2-3], 15-17 Ric II [98,mm.2-3], 19 Ric II [99,m.2], 21 Ric II [100,m.3] (1381-96).

[class KB 9/] 4-5 Hen IV [186,mm.50-51], 8-9 Hen IV [195,mm.11,38], 11-12 Hen IV [201,m.58] (1381-1411).

Sixteenth to Nineteenth Centuries

Published

J.C. Jeaffreson (ed.), *Middlesex County Records* (Old Series), 4 vols., Middx. County R.S. (1886-1892, republished G.L.C. 1972-75) include indictments, coroners' inquests-post-mortem and recogniances from 1549 to 1689.

William le Hardy (ed.), *Calendar to the County of Middlesex Sessions Records* (New Series), 4 vols. (1935-41), covering 1612-18, includes a few refs. to coroners' inquests and to the coroners themselves.

T.R. Forbes, 'Coroners' inquests in the county of Middlesex, England, 1819-42', *Journal of the History of Medicine* **32** (1977).

The National Archives.

Liberties of the Duchy of Lancaster, Middlesex.

Inquests and returns 1817-78 [DL 46/1-13], with chronological list of names 1857-78 [DL 46/21], 1878-84 [DL 46/29-34].

Disbursements 1889-95 [DL 46/42].

See also page 13 for coroners' records in King's Bench, Assizes and Chancery.

London Metropolitan Archives *(formerly G.L.R.O.).*

Note. Coroners' records are catalogued in three loose-leaf binders.

Western District [MJ/SPC.W].

Inquests 1780-88, 1799-1802, 1819-20, 1829-31, 1835-36, 1838 (most with depositions, but 1780-1 unfit for public inspection).

Calendar (TS 'Appendix'), 1780-1836, to Inquests: parish, name of deceased, verdict, remarks (but not date), a total of 1,943, keyed by number to the chronological details in main catalogue. Not indexed.

Bills 1753-58 (unfit), 1769, 1777-1814 (gaps).

Case papers 1890 on (see below).

Registers 1856-62, 1892 [COR/A/1-2,8].

Old Bailey depositions 1755-80 (gaps).

Central District [MJ/SPC.C] (formed 1862).

Registers 1862-1910 [COR/A/3-8,13].

Depositions 1862-1910 [COR/B].

Case papers 1889-97, 1899-1905, 1907-26*.

Post mortem reports 1889-1910.

Inquisition 1889.

Eastern District [MJ/SPC.E] (In 1888, divided into N.E. and S.E. Districts, but by 1892 both transferred to County of London *(q.v.)* except Tottenham and Wood Green, which formed the new **Eastern District**.)

Inquests 1781-83 (1782-3 unfit), 1785-86, 1803, 1818-38.

Calendar (TS 'Appendix', 2 vols.) 1781-1838, to Inquests, details as for Western District. 3,925 entries.

Bills 1777-1806 (gaps; 1782, 1787-8 unfit).

Old Bailey depositions 1755-81 (gaps).

Case papers from 1892 (see below).

North Eastern District.

Case papers 1888-92 (1889-92 for Tottenham and Wood Green only).

Liberties of the Duchy of Lancaster.

Bills 1789, 1828-29 (incomplete).

Case papers for Edmonton and Enfield 1884-1932*.

Liberty of Savoy.

Case papers 1885-88 (when transferred to County of London).

City and Liberty of Westminster.

Old Bailey depositions 1756-79 (gaps).

Bills 1757, 1769, 1777-84, 1814, 1819-42 (some 1757, 1819-20, 1836 and 1839 unfit for public inspection).

Middlesex *(16th-19th centuries)* continued

City of Westminster Archives Centre,
10 St Ann's Street, London SW1P 2XR.
See infomation leaflet 9, also on-line.

Western District, Paddington. Inquest records 1840-64 (incl. victims. jury lists and verdicts). Some on microfilm.
Register of bodies in the mortuary 1901-83*.

Westminster Abbey Muniments Room,
Western District. Inquests 1784 (part).
City and Liberty of Westminster. Inquests and related papers *c.*1760-1879.

Modern
(asterisked dates usually subject to 75-year closure)

Note. The City of London coroner had jurisdiction over Holloway Prison, 1852-1965*.

London Metropolitan Archives.
Western District. Case papers 1890-1952*, 1955*-1965* (names catalogued from 1960).
Central District. Case papers, see above.
Eastern District. Case papers 1892-1950*, 1954*-1965*.
Register 1959*-65*.
Liberties of the Duchy of Lancaster. Case papers, see above.

Modern coroners' records: a random 10% sample (plus significant-seeming cases) are preserved after the initial 15-year period of retention. At present this applies to records pre-1967.

MONMOUTHSHIRE

(since 1974 in WALES: Gwent)

Medieval

The National Archives.
Monmouth Borough. Roll 27-30 Hen VI [DL 41/11/5] (1448-52).

Sixteenth to Nineteenth Centuries

The National Archives. See page 13 for coroners' records in King's Bench, Assizes and Chancery.

Gwent Record Office, *Cwmbran.*
County. Inquisitions 1871-83 (unsorted, uncatalogued and fragile, therefore not yet available for public inspection).
Accounts 1861-84.
Vouchers 1795-1889.
Constables' notices 1857-83.
Monmouth Borough. Inquisitions 1822-35.

Modern
(asterisked dates usually subject to 75-year closure)

Gwent Record Office, *Cwmbran.*
Monmouthshire/Gwent. Inquest papers 1954*-79*.
Newport Borough. Inquest papers 1960*-82*.

NORFOLK

Medieval

Published
C. Gross (1896) [for JUST 2/20].
W. Hudson and J.C. Tingey (eds.), *The Records of the City of Norwich* **1** (1906) [for Case 8,a2, inquisitions 1268-85, part].
D. Owen, *The Making of King's Lynn* (Records of Social and Economic History, New Series no. IX) [for King's Lynn roll 1302-5].

The National Archives [class JUST 2/].
County. Rolls 53 Hen III - 3 Ed I [266], 9-13 Ed I [277], 29-38 Ed III [102,mm.6-19], 29-37 Ed III [102, mm.20-23], 35-45 Ed III [104], 1-3 Ric II [105] (1268-85, 1355-80).
Bishop of Ely's Liberty in Marshland. Roll 35-36 Ed III [20, pubd.] (1361-63).
Great Yarmouth Borough. 8-13 Ed I [264], 32-33 Ed III [102,m.1], 34-37 Ed III [102,mm.2-3], 37 Ed III [102,m.4] (1279-85, 1358-64).
King's Lynn Borough. 53 Hen III - 2 Ed I [263], 30-35 Ed III [102,m.24], 35-37 Ed III [103] (1268-74, 1356-64).
Norwich City. Roll 27-37 Ed III [102,mm.25-26] (1353-64).
Thetford Borough. Roll 29-37 Ed III [102,mm.4 schedule 5] (1355-64).

Norfolk Record Office, *Norwich.*
Norwich City. Roll of presentments, 1263-67 [case 8 shelf a].
Inquisitions, 1268-79, 1284-85 [case 8 shelf a, pubd.].
Great Yarmouth. Roll 1294-95, 1297-99 [Y/C 13/1].
King's Lynn. Roll of inquests 1302-5 [KL/C14, pubd.].

Sixteenth to Nineteenth Centuries

The National Archives.
Duchy of Lancaster in Norfolk. Abstracts of inquests and returns 1804-29, 1853-75, 1885-89 [DL 46/27-28].
See page 13 for coroners' records in King's Bench, Assizes and Chancery.

Norfolk Record Office, *Norwich.*
Norwich City. Inquests 1669-1719, 1723-86, 1798-1835 [case 6a] indexed calendar in preparation.
Bills re riots 1766 [case 6 shelf h].
Great Yarmouth. Inquest enrolments in Borough Sessions records 1502-3, 1509-10, 1523-4, 1531-1623, 1630-51, 1662-76 [C/4].

Modern
(asterisked dates usually subject to 75-year closure)

Norfolk Record Office, *Norwich.*
County. Notes of appointment 1878-1922.
Oaths 1870-1935; Patent books 1880-1919 [C/Scj].
Dereham District (incl. coroner to the Duchy of Lancaster in Norfolk until 1926). Letters of appointment 1880, 1919 [COR 1/1/1-2].

Norfolk *(Modern)*, Dereham District continued

Register of inquests 1853-1971* (incl., to 1953 only, place and date of death, age, occupation, depositions, verdicts, expenses) [COR 1/1/3-6].
Inquisition files: 1948 treasure trove [COR 1/3/1], 1953* flood victims [COR 1/3/3].
Inquisition files, incl. depositions and verdicts 1953*-69* [COR 1/3/3,4-21].
Home Office returns: 1904-47* [COR 1/2/1-2].

Norwich County District. The Norwich City Coroner acted as County Coroner for this area during 1977-8; the two districts were united as Norwich District on 1 October 1978.
Registers of deaths 1953*-66*, 1974*-78* [COR 2/1/1-3].
Case papers 1945*-78* (incomplete for 1960, 1964-68) [COR 2/2/1-32].
Photographs and pink forms 1978* [COR 2/2/33-4].
Correspondence 1974*-78* [COR 2/3/1].
Expense account 1963*-71* [COR 2/3/4].

Norwich City/District. Inquisitions, 1933*, 1937*-1993* [COR 3/4/1-108 + unlisted].
On men executed, 1909, 1938*, 1945* [COR 3/8/1].
Registers of inquests 1896-1980* [COR 3/1/1-20].
Home Office returns 1929*-56* (incomplete) [COR 3/2/1-16].
Daily record sheets 1955*-80*, 1987-93 [COR 3/3/1-30 + unlisted].
Photographic evidence 1955*-82* [COR 3/5/1-28]. (Later items stored with inquisitions)
Post-mortem reports ('pink forms' [sic]) 1955*-93* [COR 3/6/1-52 + unlisted].
Notices of deaths of children under 1908 Children Act, 1909-33* [COR 3/7/1].
Returns from various institutions 1916*-55*, incomplete [COR 3/7/2-22].
Various letters, warrants, recogniances, 1909-30* [COR 3/8/2].
Newcuttings books 1955*-83* [COR 3/10/1-8].
Opinions on death of John Minns of Thwaite, n.d. [COR 3/8/3].

Gt Yarmouth. Evidence book 1951*-56* [COR 4/2/1].
Case papers (incl. depositions, post mortem reports and pink forms) 1951*-91* [COR 4/3/1-105].
Daily record books 1928*-56* [COR 4/3/1-2]
Correspondence 1957*-64* [COR 4/4/1].

King's Lynn. Inquest books 1920*-29* [KL].
Home Office returns 1951*-71* [COR 5/2/1].
Appointment of deputies 1955*, 1959* [COR 5/1/1].
Case papers, incl. depositions and post-mortem reports 1950*-72*, 1975-80 [COR 5/3/1-28 + unlisted].
Sudden death files: depositions 1969*-72*, photographs 1965*-72* [COR 5/4/1-2].
Counterfoils: orders for burials 1947*-72* [COR 5/5/1], certificate 'E' 1948*-72* [COR 5/5/2], certs. issued after inquest 1949*-72* [COR 5/5/3], certs. issued to registrar, n.d. [COR 5/5/4], receipts of notice of intention to remove bodies out of England 1951*-62* [COR 5/5/5], unidentified (USAAF?) 1954*-64* [COR 5/5/6].

NORTHAMPTONSHIRE

Medieval

Published

C. Gross (1896) [for JUST 2/106(pt), 2/107(pt), 2/111(pt), 2/118(pt)].

Associated Architectural Socs., Reports & Papers **31** has translations of parts of JUST 2/106, 2/107, 2/108B, 2/111, 2/113, 2/114, 2/116, 2/117A, 2/118, 2/119A&B.

The National Archives [class JUST 2/].

County. Rolls 21 Ed I - 9 Ed II [107], 25 Ed I - 5 Ed II [120,m.17], 27 Ed I - 20 Ed II [106], 29 Ed I - 9 Ed II [640,mm.1-2], 7-8 Ed II [270], 5-10 Ed III [111,mm.1-17], 13-14 Ed III [255/4-6 & 112], 17-36 Ed III [113], 24-27,30-34 Ed III [115], 36-43 Ed III [114], 37-42 Ed III [116], 49 Ed III - 1 Ric II [117A], 49-51 Ed III [117B], 1-4 Ric II [119A&B], 3-4 Hen IV [274], 4-5 Hen IV [275], 13 Hen IV - 8 Hen V [119C] (1292-1421).

Northampton Borough. Rolls 6-8 Ed II [108A], 9-10 Ed II [108B], 50 Ed III - 1 Ric II [118,m.1], 1-3 Ric II [118,m.2] (1312-17, 1376-80).

Sixteenth to Nineteenth Centuries

The National Archives. See page 13 for coroners' records in King's Bench, Assizes and Chancery.

Northamptonshire Record Office, *Northampton.*

County (Quarter Sessions). Accounts 1899-1907 (incl. persons, date, ages, verdicts, juries, etc).
Various administrative matters, appointments, etc, 1849-1960.

Soke (or Liberty) of Peterborough (Nassaburgh Hundred). Inquest returns 1813, 1821-42, giving date, name, verdict and cause; series includes four held in Huntingdonshire [Dean and Chapter of Peterborough deposit].
Various other records, as yet unlisted, 1822, 1827, 1842-1948* [Coroner's deposit].

Index to inquests. For the following years, 1822, 1827, 1841-1844, 1846-50, 1852-1925. Name, age, verdict, close relative. Sufficient information to order a copy from the Northants Record Office. Name index to each book. Originals at the NRO. Index also at Peterborough Public Library and P'boro FHS.

Daventry. Inquests 1773-95 [Daventry Borough].

Notes relating to inquests at **Broughton**, near Kettering, 1806-46.

Modern

(asterisked dates usually subject to 75-year closure)

Northamptonshire Record Office, *Northampton.*

County. See above.

Soke of Peterborough/Nassaburgh Hundred.
Notices of deaths and doctors' reports 1922*-46*.
Registers 1928*-40*; Inquests, etc, 1963*, 1965*-71*.
See also above.

Northampton. Inquisitions, depositions, post-mortems 1915*-19*, 1921*-47*, 1949*.

NORTHUMBERLAND

Sixteenth to Nineteenth Centuries

The National Archives. See page 13 for coroners' records in King's Bench, Assizes and Chancery.

Tyne & Wear Archives Service, *Newcastle upon Tyne.*
Tynemouth, Castle Ward and **Haltwhistle**.
Notebook 1839-41 [DX427].

Berwick upon Tweed Record Office.
Berwick. Inquisitions 1745-1851 (indexed).

Modern
(asterisked dates usually subject to 75-year closure)

Northumberland Collections Service, *Ashington.*
North Northumberland.
Registers of deaths reported 1953*-78*.
Reports 1977*-79*.
South Northumberland.
Inquest files 1870-1970* (many gaps).
Early records from North N'humbd have been lost.

Tyne & Wear Archives Service, *Newcastle upon Tyne.*
Newcastle upon Tyne. Registers of deaths and court records 1939*-69* [581].

Berwick upon Tweed Record Office, *Berwick.*
Berwick. Inquisitions 1870-1951* (indexed to 1924) (some records from 1745)

NOTTINGHAMSHIRE

Until 1858, there were only two county coroners, with no geographical boundary. Nottinghamshire was then divided into three county districts: Nottingham, Newark and Retford.
See also Derbyshire, Honour of Tutbury.

Medieval

Published
A. du Boulay Hill, *East Bridgford, Notts.* (1932) [for JUST 1/689(pt), 692(pt)].

The National Archives.
County [class JUST 1/]. Rolls 4-7 Ed II [690,mm.14-17,19], 4-12 Ed III [689], 15-22 Ed III [690, mm.1-13, 18], 21-22 Ed III [692]. [class JUST 2/] 23-35 Ed III [120,mm.1-16], 36-42 Ed III [121,mm.1-9,11-18], 37-39 Ed III [KB 9/95], 40 Ed III [121,m.10], 5-15 Ric II [124], 6-15 Ric II [125-26], 17-19 Ric II [127] (1310-96).
Nottingham Borough [class JUST 2/]. 41-42 Ed III [122,m.2], 44-45 Ed III [122.m.1], 1-2 Ric II [123,m.1.], 3-15 Ric II [123,mm/2-6] (1367-92).

Sixteenth to Nineteenth Centuries

Published
R.F. Hunnisett, *Calendar of Nottinghamshire Coroners' Inquests 1485-1558*, Thoroton Society Record Series **25** (1966).
See also sections on coroners in H. Hampton Copnall, *Nottinghamshire County Records in the Seventeenth Century* (1915) and K. Tweedale Meaby, *Nottinghamshire County Records in the Eighteenth Century* (1947).

The National Archives. See page 13 for coroners' records in King's Bench, Assizes and Chancery.

Nottinghamshire Archives, *Nottingham.*
In addition to the main series of records set out below, there are a number of items dispersed among the private collections in the Record Office which are not readily identifiable with particular districts from the lists:
Warrants for summoning juries and lists of jurors in 1801 [DDM105/14].
Depositions at inquest on murder in 1801 [DDM/105/15].
County coroner papers incl. acts, orders, official circulars (1837, 1854-97) as well as inquests [DDH169/1-177].
Alterations of districts, 1856-61 [DDH169/38-58].
Accounts and financial papers, 1837-99 [DDH 169/59-97].
Papers re inquests, 1856-99 [DDH169/98-108; DDH169/145-160].
Misc. items re Coroners' Society, etc, 1855-91 [DDH169/161-74; see also CR 13/1].
Inquests, incl. verdicts, inventories of goods, minutes of evidence, etc, pre-1769 [DDP65/69-71].
Deaths in coal pits at Greasley 1808 and Trowell 1817 [DDE8/25, 28].
Report on body in Trent at South Muskham 1883 [DDH125/18].
Arrears account 1742 [DD3P 19/1].
Death of a Nottingham judge 1884 [DD 368].
Unlisted correspondence, returns of death, court fees, population, etc, 1833-48.
Poster re candidature for county coroner 1855.
Order in Council giving parishes contained within the three districts, 1858 [CR 12/1].

Nottingham City. Inquests 1732-76 [CA 551-689], 1816-36 [CA 690-1245]. Calendar includes year, name, description, cause of death; jury not calendared.
Newark Borough. Inquisitions (incl. verdict and signatures of coroner and jury) 1898-99 [DDH 169/109-144].
Papers 1875-78 [DDH 169/175-77].
Retford. Unlisted inquests and legal affidavits 1833-1835.

Nottinghamshire continued

Modern
(asterisked dates usually subject to 75-year closure)

Nottinghamshire Archives, *Nottingham.*

Nottinghamshire County:
Inquests 1981*-90 [C/CR 1/6].
Non-inquests 1981*-90*.
Tapes of inquest proceedings 1983-90 [C/CR 1/7].
Rampton Hospital inquests 1967-77 [C/CR 1/8], non-inquests 1967-78 (arr. alphabetically).
Register of deaths 1981-88 [C/CR4/7/1-13].
Daily records 1987-90 [C/CR6/2/1-16].

County Districts:
Newark (incl. **Newark Borough** after 1974).
Inquests 1939*, 1942*-78* [CR1/2].
Non-inquests 1960*-78* [CR2/2].
Registers of deaths 1930*-53* [CR4/1/1], 1953*-1961* [CR4/3/1-3].
Daily records 1960*-4*, 1969*-79* [CR6/1/3,10-17].
Returns, 1899-1923 [CR9/2/1].
Registers of fees and dsibursements 1899-1958* [CR10/2/1].
Appointments 1888-1924* [CR11/1/1].
Nottingham District. Inquests 1938*-9*, 1943*, 1945*, 1947*-76* (incomplete) [CR1/3].
Non-inquest 1949*-51*, 1956*-76* (incomplete) [CR2/3].
Registers of deaths 1957*-81* [CR4/4/1-7].
Daily records 1956*-58*, 1960*-63*, 1969*-78* [CR 6/1/1.2,4,12,14-156] (other daily records are available, but the places are unclear).
Retford District. Inquests 1945*-79, 1981-2* [CR 1/5].
Non-inquests 1945*-66* [CR2/4].
Police and post-mortem reports 1970*-75* [CR 3/2].
Registers of deaths 1953*-81* [CR4/6/1-11].
Correspondence and miscellaneous papers 1949*-71* [C/CR 17].
Newark Borough (see county district above after 1974). Inquests 1942*-74* [CR1/1].
Non-inquests 1960*-74* [CR2/1].
Registers of deaths 1930*-53* [CR4/1/1], 1953*-1961* [CR4/2/1-2].
Registers of fees and disbursements 1929*-58* [C/CR10/1/1
Daily records 1960*-70* [CR6/1/7,10,12,13].
Returns 1889-1923 [CR9/1/1].
Registers of fees and disbursements 1929*-58* [CR10/1/1].
Appointments 1888-1924 [CR11/1/1].
Nottingham City. Inquests, 1939*, 1948*-81* (incomplete) [CR1/4].
Non-inquests 1957*, 1967-81*
Police and post mortem reports 1967*-78* [CR3/1].
Registers of deaths 1896-19681* [CR4/5/1-35].
Record of cases 1898-1970* [CR 5/1/1-8].
Jury lists, 1920*-38*, 1948*-64* [CR7/1/1-2].
Returns 1894-1932* [CR9/3/1].
Miscellaneous (incl. correspondence, appoint-ments, depositions, etc, 1890-1943* [CR14/1-7].
Coroner's role in wartime 1928*-45* [CATC 10/114/12/1-2].

Also closed for 75 years are the results of an investigation into the ages of suicides, and lists of suicides and persons drowned.

OXFORDSHIRE

Medieval

Published
H.E. Salter (ed.), *Records of Mediaeval Oxford: Coroners' Inquests, etc* (1912) [for translations of parts of JUST 2/128, 129, 133, 135, 137].
H.E. Salter (ed.*), Snappe's Formulary and other records* (Oxford Hist. Soc. **80**) [for Roll 25-29 Ed I (1296-1301), in Oxfordshire Archives].
J.E.T. Rogers (ed.), *Oxford City Documents, 1268-1665*, Oxford H.S. **18** [for Oxon. Roll 30 in Bodleian].
C. Gross (1896) [for parts of JUST 2/128, 132, 136].

The National Archives [class JUST 2/].
County. Rolls 52 Hen III - 5 Ed I [261], 20-34 Ed III [130], 36-37,40-42,45 Ed III [131], 42 Ed III - 7 Ric II [132], 45-46 Ed III [KB 9/98A,m.46], 1-12 Ric II [134], 12-15 Ric II [136], 15-19 Ric II [138], 15-21 Ric II [140], 19-21 Ric II [141] (1267-77, 1346-98).
Northgate Hundred (Oxford). Rolls 51 Ed III - 5 Ric II [133,mm.1-2], 5-21 Ric II [133,mm.3-6] (1377-98).
Oxford Borough. Rolls 25-26 Ed I [128], 15-22 Ed III [129], 7-8 Ric II [255/11], 9-12 Ric II [135], 12-21 Ric II [137] (1383-98).

Bodleian Library, *Oxford.*
Oxford. Roll 29-31 Ed I [Oxon Roll 30; published].

Oxfordshire Record Office, *Cowley, Oxford.*
Oxford Borough. Rolls 25-29 Ed I (1296-1301) [uncatalogued: formerly in the Bridgwater Corporation papers, Somerset Record Office, which has a transcript, ref. D/B/bw, Dilks's cat., vol. i; published];
29 Ed I - 1 Ed II (1300-08) [I,26,1-4].

Sixteenth to Nineteenth Centuries

Published: Oxon Coroners Inquests 1820-37 (3 pts), Oxfordshire Black Sheep Publications, 2008 (from Quarter Sessions bills and other sources).
The National Archives. See page 13 for coroners' records in King's Bench, Assizes and Chancery.

Oxfordshire Record Office, *Cowley, Oxford.*
Oxford City and Central. Inquest files (incl. depositions) 1844-77.
Oxford Central. Inquest files (incl. depositions) 1877-1905.
Kidlington. Single inquisition 1711.

Oxfordshire continued

Note. A scrapbook of newspaper cuttings kept by the coroner for Northern Oxon. District in the late 19th century exists, but has been mislaid. If rediscovered it will be deposited at Oxfordshire Record Office.

Modern
(asterisked dates usually subject to 75-year closure)

Oxfordshire Record Office, *Cowley, Oxford.*
Oxford City and Central. Inquest files 1973*-92*.
Oxford Central. Inquest files 1929*-74*.
Oxford City. Inquest files (incl. depositions), 1901-1904, 1907-16*, 1919*-56*, 1958*-74*.
North Oxon. Inquest files (incl. depositions) 1912-1963*.
North/Western Oxon. Inquest files (incl. depositions) 1964*-75*.
Banbury District. Inquest files (incl. depositions) 1964*-73*.

RUTLAND

Sixteenth to Nineteenth Centuries

The National Archives. See page 13 for coroners' records in King's Bench, Assizes and Chancery.

Lincolnshire Archives, *Lincoln.*
Stamford and South Rutland. Inquests 1894-1909.

Modern
(asterisked dates usually subject to 75-year closure)

Record Office for Leicestershire, Leicester and Rutland, *Wigston Magna.*
County. (All other records pre-1974 destroyed.)
Reports on inquests 1954*-63* [RCO/1-10].
Reports on sudden deaths 1954*-62* [RCO/11/1-158].
Day book 1930*-51* [RCO/12]

SHROPSHIRE

Medieval

Published
C. Gross (1896) [for JUST 2/147(pt)].
Shropshire Arch. & Nat. Hist. Soc., 3rd series, **5** (1905) [for Acc 3365/2689].

The National Archives [class JUST 2/].
County. Rolls 33-42 Ed III [142], 49-51 Ed III [255/9], 1-16 Ric II [144], 16 Ric II - I Hen IV [146,m.2-6], 17 Ric II - 3 Hen IV [147], 1 Hen IV - 2 Hen V [148], 1-5 Hen IV [145,m.2], 2-5 Hen IV [145,m.1], 6-10 Hen IV [149], 6,9-14 Hen IV [150], 6 Hen IV - 1 Hen V [151], 1-2 Hen V [145,m.12] (1359-1415).
Shrewsbury Borough. Rolls 1-9 Ric II, 1 Hen IV [143,mm.1-2], 10-11 Ric II, 1 Hen IV - 1 Hen V [145,mm.3-11,13], 16 Ric II [146,m.1] (1377-1414).

Shropshire *(Medieval)* continued

Shropshire Archives, *Shrewsbury.*
Shrewsbury Borough. Roll 24034 Ed I (1295-1306) [Acc 3365/2689].

Sixteenth to Nineteenth Centuries

Published
L.J. Lee and R.G. Venables, *The full List and partial Abstract of the Quarter Sessions Rolls 1696-1820* contains summaries of coroners' returns from 1755 and from 1780 abstracts of the returns more or less complete.

The National Archives. See page 13 for coroners' records in King's Bench, Assizes and Chancery.

Shropshire Archives, *Shrewsbury.*
County. Inquests (bills?) are filed on the county Quarter Sessions rolls from 1755 onwards [Q/S].
Wellington District. Inquisition books 1855-71 [14/2/1-2].
Bridgnorth Borough. Inquests c.1650-1836 (consecutive from 1765).
Appointments 1787, 1789.
Miscellaneous 19th century papers [4001/J/1].
Ludlow Borough. Precepts to summon jury, jury lists, depositions, and inquests 1551-1839 [LB/12].
Shrewsbury Borough. Curia parva rolls have inquests and jurors' lists 1562-1697 (sporadic).
Court of Record rolls have inquests 1623-1700 *passim.*
Quarter Sessions rolls have inquests (bills?) for the 18th and 19th centuries [3365/].
Wenlock Borough.
Inquisitions, 1616, 1664-67, 1702-03, 1725-26, 1735, 1745, 1751-59, 1804-36; 1917*-27*.

Modern
(asterisked dates usually subject to 75-year closure)

Shropshire Archives, *Shrewsbury.*
East Shropshire. Inquests and papers 1960*-90*.
West Shropshire District.
Inquests and papers 1955*-74*.
North Shropshire District.
Inquests and papers 1955*-74*.
South Shropshire District.
Inquests and papers 1955*-81* [4780].
Bridgnorth and Much Wenlock.
Records 1945*-1963* [2412].
Mid and North West Division.
Inquests and papers 1955*-74*.

SOMERSET

Medieval

Published

County (West Somerset) coroners' roll 1315 in *Somerset & Dorset Notes & Queries* **31**, p.322 (1985) [S.R.O. DD/L P31/1].

Somerset Archive & Record Service, *Taunton.*
County (West Somerset). Roll 1315-1321 [DD/L P31/1, published].

Sixteenth to Nineteenth Centuries

The National Archives. See page 13 for coroners' records in King's Bench, Assizes and Chancery.

Somerset Archive & Record Service, *Taunton.*
Bridgwater Borough. Inquisitions 1718-51 [D/B/bw.1917/1-69].
Langport Borough. *c.*100 inquisitions 1718-1751.
South-Eastern Division. Coroner's account 1872-86.

Bath & North East Somerset Record Office, *Bath.*
Bath. Examinations and inquests 1776-1835 (indexed from 1798).

Modern
(asterisked dates usually subject to 75-year closure)

Somerset Archive & Record Service, *Taunton.*
Northern Division. Inquests 1926*-73*; daily records 1928*-72* (this Division ended in 1974).
South Eastern Division, Inquests 1929*-date*.
Western Division. Inquests 1932*-date*.
Accounts 1932*-1950*.
?County. Inquests, 1999-2002.

Bath & North East Somerset Record Office, *Bath.*
Bath. Inquests and inquisitions 1929*-50*, 1960*-1962*, 1968*-73*.
Register of inquests (with index) 1900-49* (except 1927-28).
Correspondence 1916*-49*, 1951*.
Correspondence re air raid deaths 1942*.
Notices of death (institutions) 1929*-49*.
Certificates after inquest and notifications to registrar, inquest unnecessary 1928*-52*.
Removal of bodies out of England 1924*-51* (incomplete).
Certificates for cremation 1934*-51*.
Statistical returns 1929*-41*, 1944*-49*.
Expenses 1931*-50*.

STAFFORDSHIRE

See also Derbyshire. Honour of Tutbury.

Medieval

Published

C. Gross (1896) [for parts of JUST 2/163, 166, 168].
William Salt Arch. Soc. **16** [for abstract of part of JUST 2/167].

The National Archives [class JUST 2/].
County. Rolls 4 Ed III [159], 37-46 Ed III [112], 47 Ed III - Ric II [160], 4-15 Ric II [161], 6-9,20 Ric II [165,m.2], 8-9 Ric II, 1-13 Hen IV [162], 9-16 Ric II [163], 10-22 Ric II [164], 13-16,22 Ric II [165,m.1], 19-22 Ric II [165,m.4], 19-20 Ric II [165,m.3], 20 Ric II - 1 Hen IV [166], 22 Ric II - 13 Hen IV [167], 11-14 Hen IV [168], 11 Hen IV - 1 Hen V [KB 9/200,m.45], 1 Hen V [169], ?Hen V [170] (1330-1, 1363-1414).

Sixteenth to Nineteenth Centuries

The National Archives. See page 13 for coroners' records in King's Bench, Assizes and Chancery.

Staffordshire Record Office, *Stafford.*
Stafford. Registers of inquests 1861-1950* [D1298].
Lichfield. Eight inquests 1817-39 [D(W)1553/72-80; formerly in the William Salt Library].

Wolverhampton Archives and Local Studies, *Wolverhampton.*
Wolverhampton. Records of coroner's court late 19th century - *1989 (early reports incomplete).

Modern
(asterisked dates usually subject to 75-year closure)

Staffordshire Record Office, *Stafford.*
See above.
In the modern period, registers, indexes, and census-year only post-mortem and inquest files are preserved. The national destruction schedules are adhered to (see Introduction).

Walsall Local History Centre, *Walsall.*
Walsall. Records of the coroner's court 1910-65*.
Name index to records 1910-18

Wolverhampton: see above.

SUFFOLK

Medieval

Published
C. Gross (1896) [for JUST 2/173(pt)].

The National Archives [class JUST 2/].
County. Rolls 26-31 Ed III [173], 28-31 Ed III [175,177], 28-30 Ed III [176], 28-29 Ed III [174], 29-35 Ed III [179A], 35-37 Ed III [178,mm.9-11] (1352-64).
Liberty of Bury St Edmunds. Rolls 30-38 Ed III [178,mm.1,3-8] (1356-65).
Lothingland Half-Hundred. Roll 36-37 Ed III [178,m.12] (1362-64).
Dunwich Borough (here, the bailiff was also coroner). Roll 37 Ed III [178,m.2] (1363-64).
Ipswich Borough. Roll 33-38 Ed III [178,mm.13-15] (1359-65).

Sixteenth to Nineteenth Centuries

Published
Sudden Deaths in Suffolk. A Survey of Coroners' Records, Pt 1. 1767-1858; Pt 2 1859-1920, Leslie and Doreen Smith, Suffolk FHS, 1995, 1997 (£3.50 each incl. p&p; orders to Suffolk FHS, c/o Elizabeth Arkieson, 8 The Crescents, Reydon, Southwold, Suffolk IP18 6RT).
These cover the **Liberty of St Etheldreda** (Hundreds of Carlford, Colneis, Loes, Plomesgate, Thredling and Wilford), and includes an indexes of over 2,000 names of all those on whom inquests were held.

The National Archives. See page 13 for coroners' records in King's Bench, Assizes and Chancery.

Suffolk Record Office, *Ipswich.*
County (East Suffolk). Appointments 1859-1963* [345].
Correspondence 1860-84 [346].
Maps of Coroners' Districts, 19th century [343].
Ipswich Borough. Minutes of inquests 1869-84 [DG 1].
Borough of Aldeburgh. Inquests 1817, 1828, 1866-1872, 1878, 1880-81 [EE1/L1; EE1/P1; HB 10: 50/20/18].
Liberty of St Etheldreda (Liberty of the Dean and Chapter of Ely in the hundreds of Carlford, Colneis, Plomesgate, Loes, Wilford and Thredling) [HB 50/20/8-12]. See Publications above.
Appointments 1754-1846.
Inquests 1785-1858.
Counterfoils, orders for burial 1837-56.
Papers re bills 1801-57.
Papers re specific cases 1826-51.
Accounts of receipts 1837-58.
Papers re Coroners' Society 1843-58.

Suffolk Record Office, *Bury St Edmunds.*
Bury St Edmunds. Borough Inquests 1686-1809 [D8/5/1-7].
Schedule of fees 1837 [D8/5/8].

Modern
(asterisked dates usually subject to 75-year closure)

Suffolk Record Office, *Ipswich.*
County (East Suffolk C.C.). Appointments: East Suffolk 1859-1963* [345]; West Suffolk 1912-1940* [3134/366-369].
Inquest certificates 1922*-51* [348].
Orders under Coroners (Amendment) Act (1926), 1934*-84* [344].
Southern Division [EC 1]. Inquisitions, etc, 1918*-1973*.
Daily record books 1964*-74*.
Eastern Division [EC 2]. Registers 1934*-56*, 1963*-68*.
Inquisitions, etc, 1951*-65*.
Statistical returns 1934-51.
Northern Division [EC 3]. Inquisitions, depositions, reports, 1946*; 1948*-74*.
Register 1968*-74*.
Ipswich Borough [DG 1,2]. Minutes of inquests 1925*-27*.
Inquisitions, evidences, depositions, 1931*-73*.
Registers 1931*-72*.
Ipswich Division [EC 4]. Inquisitions, depositions, reports, 1974*-82*.
Registers 1975*-82*.
Index book 1975*-78*.
Liberty of Etheldreda. Inquests 1911-33* [East Suffolk CC 341].
Notices of death of inmates of Suffolk District Lunatic Asylum 1877-1933* [East Suffolk CC 342].

Suffolk Record Office, *Bury St Edmunds.*
West Suffolk District. Inquests 1963*-72* [EC500]

Note. There are no coroners' records at the Lowestoft branch of the Suffolk Record Office.

SURREY

Before 1889, this section relates to the whole historic county, except for the Borough of Southwark, for which see under 'London'. From 1888 those places transferred to the newly created County of London will be found under 'London'. Places incorporated into Greater London in 1965 will be found under their former counties.

A description of the history of coroners' jurisdictions is available in the Surrey Record Office. The county was divided into Eastern and Western districts in 1825, with a shift of boundary in 1878. Five new districts were created in 1883: Newington, Camberwell, Croydon, Kingston and Guildford, the first two being transferred to the L.C.C. in 1888. Since 1965 there has been a single coroner for the whole county, though Guildford retained its own coroner until 1974.

The Royal Borough of Kingston had a coroner from 'early times', but it is unclear when the arrangement terminated.

Medieval

The National Archives.

County. Rolls 5 Hen V [KB 9/210,m.39] (1417-8), 29 Hen VI [KB 9/265,m.33] (1450-1).

Sixteenth to Nineteenth Centuries

Published

J.S. Cockburn, *Calendar of Assize Records: Surrey Indictments*, 1558-1625 (1980, 1982) [for ASSI 35, see pages 12-13].

The National Archives. See also page 13 for coroners' records in King's Bench, Assizes [ASSI 35] and Chancery.

Surrey History Centre, *Woking .*

County. Bills, incl. names of deceased, among the 18th century Quarter Sessions records, from 1751 [QS 2/6].

Eastern Division. A few inquest records for 1867 only [2557/1-30].

Kingston Museum & Heritage Service.

Kingston upon Thames Borough. Inquests 1664-1825 [RBK KE3/1/1-152].

Documents re burial warrants 1735-49 [KE3/2/1-11].

Draft warrant summoning jury, late 17th century [KE3/3/3].

There are also some Borough coroner's accounts in the county Quarter Sessions bundles [QS 2/6], from 1791.

London Metropolitan Archives *(formerly G.L.R.O.), 40 Northampton Road, London.*

Clapham (Duchy of Lancaster). Papers 1884-89.

Corporation of London Records Office

For **Southwark**, see under 'London', page30.

Modern
(asterisked dates usually subject to 75-year closure)

Surrey History Centre, *Woking.*

County. Reports of deaths and inquests 1932* (pt) [58/22/1].

Notice of single death, Cane Hill mental hospital 1900 [58/22/2].

Registers from 1965*: to be deposited [630/1].

Papers 1965*-75* [630/2], 1976*-continuing.

East Surrey. Register 1933*-42* [607/1/1-5].

Papers (incl. treasure trove) 1934*-60* (incomplete) [607/2].

West Surrey. Register 1948*-61* [606/1].

Papers (incl. treasure trove) 1934*-65* (incomplete) [606/2].

Reigate Division. Inquests, depositions, warrants, signed inquisitions 1909 (pt) [2557/31-60].

Register 1913*-33* [629/1].

Papers 1925*-33* (incomplete) [929/2].

Guildford Division. Papers 1925*-33* [631].

Guildford. Registers of deaths 1953*-74* [RB980/2428, and 2945].

Inquiry and inquest papers 1950*-61*, sampled [RB980/2428], 1965*-71* [RB980/2428], 1971*-1974* [1945].

Croydon Central Library (Local History).

Croydon Borough. Inquests (open verdicts only) 1927*-36*.

Inquest records 'apparently full' 1940*-45*.

Since 1965, records of the Croydon coroner have been deposited with London Metropolitan Archives.

SUSSEX

In practice, county coroners have always had jurisdiction in either East or West Sussex. Apart from modern records, surviving locally held material is in the East Sussex Record Office.

Medieval

Published

The county is particularly well served by research by R.F. Hunnisett, whose publications include:

The Medieval Coroner (1961), based on his Oxford D.Phil. Thesis, 'The Medieval Coroner 1194-1487, with particular reference to the county of Sussex'.

'Sussex Coroners in the Middle Ages', *Sussex Archaeological Collections* **95.**42-58, **96.**17-34, **98.**44-70 (1957-60). These incorporate calendars of all surviving Sussex coroners' cases before 1500 then known, and a list of county and franchise coroners and their clerks, with an essay on jurisdictions.

'The last Sussex abjurations', *S.A.C.* **102**, 39-51 (1964).

East Sussex Record Office, *Lewes.*

Eastern Division. Single inquest 1398 [AMS 5592/114].

See also publications, above.

Sussex continued

Fifteenth to Nineteenth Centuries

Published

R.F. Hunnisett, *Sussex Coroners' Inquests: 1485-1558*, Sussex Record Soc. 74 (1985); *1558-1603*, P.R.O. (1996); *1603-1688* (P.R.O., 1998); *East Sussex 1688-1838*, Sussex Record Soc. 89 (2005).

J.S. Cockburn, *Calendar of Assize Records: Sussex Indictments*, 1558-1625 (1975, 1976) [for ASSI 35, see pages 12-13].

The National Archives. See page 13 for coroners' records in King's Bench, Assizes [ASSI 35] and Chancery.

EAST SUSSEX

The present Lewes District (to which Brighton Borough was added in 1974) was formed in 1891 out of the former Eastern Division of Sussex, which had itself been increased by the gradual amalgamations with much earlier borough and franchise jurisdictions: those of the Archbishop of Canterbury (in existence since 1463) and the Duchy of Lancaster (by 1479) in the 1550's; those of Pevensey, Seaford and Winchelsea boroughs in 1886; and Rye in 1888.

The other part of the Eastern division became, in 1891, the Rye District, to which were added the jurisdictions of Battle Liberty (1255), Foxearle Hundred (?1436), Gostrow Hundred (1448), Hastings Rape (1455), the Bishop of Chichester (1502), and Robertsbridge Hundred (date of origin unknown), all in 1940; and Hastings Borough (1194) in 1974. In practice, these smaller jurisdictions were held jointly by the coroner of Hastings Rape from at least 1830.

In 1986, the boundary between the two districts was adjusted to reduce their former imbalance in size.

(The above summarises an excellent introduction to the history of coronership, particularly relating to East Sussex, copyright East Sussex Record Office.)

East Sussex Record Office, *Lewes.*

County. Bills 1752-1820's [QR and QCC2]. See publications, above.

Eastern Division. Single inquest c.1548 [SAS/CP183/f75v].

Rape of Hastings (incl. parishes of Battle, Ashburnham, Herstmonceux, Watling, Brede, Udimore, Bexhill and Salehurst) [SHE].
- Single inquests kept as precedents, 1759-1845.
- Home Office and QS returns 1827-62.
- Counterfoil orders for burial 1838-52.
- Inquest papers with depositions 1848-9, 1859-66.

Hastings Borough (incl. Liberties). Single inquests 1665, 1667 (2), 1771 [Hastings Museum, C/B K1-4].
- Inquests from 1598 in Court Books.
- Town Clerk's accounts for holding inquests 1818-1835 [PAR 367 26/1/1-2].

Pevensey Borough (incl. Liberties). Inquest papers with depositions 1754-1884 [PEV 409-485].

Pevensey Rape (Duchy of Lancaster). 2 inquests, 1577 [SAS box 1].

Rye Borough (incl. Liberties). Single inquests 1487 [RYE 60/3 f.63v], 1530 [RYE 60/5 f.195].
- Inquests entered in assembly minutes, 1547-*c.*1660.
- Inquest papers with depositions 1608-1855 [RYE 32].
- Precedent book 1806-c.1825 [SHE].
- Notes on expenses 1844-63 [RYE 70/0].

Seaford Borough and Liberties. Single inquest. n.d. (pre 1573) [SEA 5].
- Inquest expenses 1847-51 [SEA 325-7].

Winchelsea Borough and Liberties. Single inquest 1582 [WIN 53 f.176].
- Inquest papers 1775-1884 [WIN 513-606].
- Inquest papers 1816-56, 1829 [DAP box 70, 319]
- Home Office returns and counterfoil books 1873-85 [WIN 607-12].
- Vouchers for jury expenses 1824-67 [WIN 613].

Battle Parish (Liberty). Single inquests 1486, 1507 [Huntingdon Library BA Vol.5, 2232, 2484] (subsequently in Rape of Hastings above).

Modern
(asterisked dates usually subject to 75-year closure)

East Sussex Record Office, *Lewes.*

County. Minutes (1890-92) and correspondence (1890-93) of regulating committee (with West Sussex) [C/C11/17, C/C83/1; see also C/C54/5(3),(9)].
- Appointments n.d. [QDA4] and 1890-1928 [C/C38].
- Related correspondence 1891-1908, 1931 [C/C55 9B,15,184].
- Correspondence re franchise coroners, appointments, etc, 1902-6, 1916-19 [C/C55/22,51].
- Case re jurisdiction outside specified area (Rye), 1874 [C/c106/1].

Lewes District. Inquest papers (incl. depositions and post mortems) 1914-27*, 1938*-85*.
- Home Office returns 1928*-47*.
- Daily record 1948*-85*.

Rye District. Inquest papers 1895-1934* [DAP box 302], 1940*-60* [SHE], 1960*-84* [MIB].

Rape of Hastings. Inquest papers with depositions and post-mortem reports 1925*-40* [SHE].

Brighton Borough. Inquest papers with depositions and post-mortem reports 1901-74*.
- Daily record 1936*-74*.
- Register of deaths reported 1953*-74*.

Hastings Borough. Inquest papers, with depositions and post-mortems 1960*-74*.

WEST SUSSEX
(see also East Sussex)

West Sussex Record Office, *Chichester.*

Chichester District; Horsham District; amalgamated into **West Sussex District** in 1969.
- Registers of deaths from 1935*.
- Case files (sampled) from 1953*.

WARWICKSHIRE

See also Derbyshire, Honour of Tutbury.

Medieval

Published

C. Gross (1696) [for JUST 2/183(pt)].

R.F. Hunnisett, 'The reliability of inquisitions as historical evidence', in D.A. Bullough and R.L. Storey (eds.), *The Study of Medieval Records: Essays in honour of Kathleen Major* (1971) [for JUST 2/184(pt), JUST 2/255/8].

Miscellanca Genealogica et Heraldica, 5th series **7** [for JUST 2/180(pt)].

The National Archives [class JUST 2/].

County. Rolls 30-33,42 Ed III [181], 39-41,46-47 Ed III [184], 45 Ed III [185,m.1], 3-9 Ric II [188,mm.1-3], 7-9 Ric II [188,m.4], 10 Ric II [189,m.4], 10 Ric II [189,m.1], 11-14 Ric II [189,mm.4-5], 11-15 Ric II [190,mm.1-3], 12-15 Ric II [189,m.6], 12,16-21 Ric II [190,mm.4-5], 14-15 Ric II [191,m.1], 16 Ric II [192,m.1], 18-21 Ric II [192,m.1], 18-21 Ric II [192,m.2], 21 Ric II [255/15] (1356-98).

Barlichway Hundred. Roll 46,50 Ed III, 2-9 Ric II [186] (1372-86).

Hemlingford Hundred. Roll 46 Ed III - 1 Ric II [185,m.2] (1372-78).

Kington Hundred. Roll 39-40 Ed III [183] (1365-67).

Knightlow Hundred. Rolls 46-47 Ed III [255/8], 1-9 Ric II [187] (1372-86).

Coventry Borough. Rolls 29-32 Ed III [180], 36-38 Ed III [182], 11-13 Ric II [189,mm.2-3], 14-20 Ric II [191,mm.2-8] (1355-97).

Sixteenth to Nineteenth Centuries

The county was divided into three districts (Northern, Central and Southern) in 1844; separate coroners had jurisdictions in Coventry (until 1847 when it became part of the Northern District), Birmingham (from 1835), Sutton Coldfield and Warwick.

The National Archives. See page 13 for coroners' records in King's Bench, Assizes and Chancery.

Warwick County Record Office, *Warwick.*

Southern District. Registers 1865-1901 [CR 1399], 1874-96, 1893-1905 [CR 449/1/22-23].

Case files 1865-66 [CR 449/1/21A].

Inquisitions with case papers 1836-50, 1864, 1869(1), 1916(1), 1917(1) [CR 1367].

Warwick Borough (also referred to **as Mid-Warwickshire District** and, inaccurately, as **Central**).

Registers 1837-1966* [CR 1769/45-47].

Inquisitions 1836-49, 1859-64 [CR 1367].

Shakespeare Centre Library and Archive, *Stratford upon Avon.*

County. *c.*500 papers, mainly inquests, 1816-50 [ER 10/5/1-494].

Stratford upon Avon Borough. *c.*30 inquests, *c.*1600-1750 [BRU 15].

Coventry City Record Office.

Coventry (the Coventry coroner was elected by the Court Leet until 1842, when the city came under the jurisdiction of the county coroners, Northern and Central Divisions).

Minute book 1728-52 [136].

Nottinghamshire Archives, *Nottingham.*

County. Application for post of county coroner for Warwickshire 1792 [DDE 3/46].

Memoranda and formulary for coroner of Warwickshire 1560-90 [DDE 67/1].

A transcription and index to inquests for Birmingham and Warwickshire (and any subsequent murder trials) reported in the *Warwick and Warwickshire Advertiser* from 1806 to 1820 and beyond, is being prepared by Mrs Pauline Page; enquiries, with SAE, may be sent to her at 218 Wake Green Road, Moseley, Birmingham B13 9QE.

Modern
(asterisked dates usually subject to 75-year closure)

In 1931-2, Coventry once again made its own appointments of coroners, and district boundaries were redrawn, the Southern District becoming the South-Western. The borough of Warwick had a separate coroner 1951-66. In 1974 (when the Birmingham and Coventry area became the county of West Midlands), the remaining county of Warwickshire was divided into the Northern and Southern Districts, and in 1979, the whole county was united under one coroner.

Warwick County Record Office.

County. Register 1986* [CR2763/1]

Case files 1986*-97* [CR2763/3, 2995, 3229]

Northern District. Case files 1911-38*, 1940*-42 [QS 8/9/1-31], 1943*-44* [CR 810/1-2], 1945*-48* [CR 293/1-4], 1949*-50* [CR 549/1-2], 1951*-53* [CR 548/1-3], 1954*-55* [CR 635/1-2], 1956*-61* [CR 1099/1-6], 1962*-1964* [CR 1242/1-3], 1965*-69* [CR 1532/1-5], 1970*-72* [CR 1743/1-3], 1973*-75* [CR 1953/1-4], 1976*-77* [CR 2153/1-2], 1978*-84* [CR 2608, 2706, 2763].

Registers 1967-85 [CR 2608, 2706, 2763].

Southern (later **South-Western**) **District.**

Regs 1931*-74* [CR 1399], 1979*-85* [CR2824].

Inquisitions (mostly filed with case files) 1939*-45* [CR 1399/Box 23], 1946*-55* [CR 1399/Boxes 9-18], 1956*-74* [CR 1642/1-19], 1974*-77* [CR 24/37-40], 1978* [CR 1919/7 and CR 2115/1]; 1979* [CR 2214].

Case files 1931*-63* [CR 1399/Boxes 1-22], 1943* [CR 449/1/21B]; 1956*-74* [CR 1642/1-19], 1974*-77* [CR 1919/3-6]; 1977* [CR 2021], 1978* [CR 2115/1], 1979* [CR 2214/1], 1980*-1982* [CR 2259], 1983-85 [CR2824].

Papers, certificates 1972*-79* [CR2115/2-3].

Warwickshire *(Modern)* continued

Central District. Registers (two overlapping series) 1900-60* [CR 1769/1-2], 1937*-64* [CR 1769/3-7].
Inquisition forms, filed in vols., 1900-41* [QS 8/10/1-34]; 1942*-74* [CR 24/1-32].
Case files 1936*-45*, 1947*-71* [CR 1769/8-44]; 1972*-74* [CR 1919/1-3]; 1970*, 1973* [CR 1950/12].
Warwick Borough (and see above). Inquisitions 1931*-37* [CR 1950/2-8]; 1939*-41* [CR 1769/49-51]; 1949*-66* [CR 24/33-36].
Case files 1937*, 1939*-64* [CR 1769/48-74]; 1946* [CR 1950/10].
Registers 1837-1966*.

Birmingham Central Library, Archive & Heritage.
Birmingham. Inquests 1875-1981* (index in progress; 1875-77 only so far).
Reports of deaths, non-inquest 1893, 1926*-34*.
Depositions 1875-78. 1880-86, 1888.
Miscellaneous papers 1874-1926*.
Solihull. Inquests 1974*-82*.

Coventry City Archives.
Coventry. Register 1958*-63*.
Inquest files 1947*-83*.
Non-inquest files 1947-49, 1969-70, 1972, 1975, 1981.

WESTMORLAND

Sixteenth to Nineteenth Centuries

The National Archives. See page 13 for coroners' records in King's Bench, Assizes and Chancery.

Cumbria Record Office, *Kendal.*
Appleby Borough. Three inquests 1724-36 [WD/Hoth/Box 35].
Appleby and North Westmorland. Inquests 1873, 1875-1922* [WTCR/NW].
Kendal and South Westmorland. Book of depositions 1835-41 [WD/K1965].

Modern
(asterisked dates usually subject to 75-year closure)

Cumbria Record Office, *Kendal.*
Kendal and South Westmorland. Files of inquests and reported deaths 1944*-74* (indexed).
Registers of deaths reported 1953*-70*.
Daily record book 1956*-67* [all WTCR/SW].
Note. A register of inquests 1928*-44* is known to have existed up to 1962, but is now missing.
Cumbria (South Division). Inquest files 1974-95.
Registers of deaths reported 1970-94 [WTCR/SW].

WILTSHIRE

Medieval

Published
C. Gross (1896) [for parts of JUST 2/201, 2/204, 2/205].

The National Archives [class JUST 2/].
County. Rolls 12-14 Ed III [193], 15-22 Ed III [194], 15-28 Ed III [195], 25-26 Ed III [197], 42 Ed III -1 Ric II [200], 1-2 Ric II [201], 2-6 Ric II [202], 2-7 Ric II [203,mm.1-12] (1338-84).
Abbot of Battle's Liberty of Bromham. Roll 7 Ric II [203,m.13] (1383-4).
Devizes Borough. Roll 6-7 Ric II [205] (1382-4).
Salisbury City. Rolls 35-51 Ed III [199], 5-7 Ric II [204,mm.1-2] (1361-84).
Wilton Borough. Roll 20,31,33,35 Ed III [196] (1346-62).

Sixteenth to Nineteenth Centuries

Published
R.F. Hunnisett, *Wiltshire Coroners' Bills 1752-1796*, Wiltshire Record Soc. **36** (1981).
R.F. Hunnisett, 'Eighteenth century coroners and their clerks', *Wiltshire Arch. & Natural Hist. Soc.* **76** (1982 for 1981).
Jean A. Cole, *Coroners' Records of a Borough: Marlborough, Wilts., 1773 to 1835.* Wilts FHS, 1993.
Jean A. Cole, *Coroners' Inquisitions for the Borough of Malmesbury, 1830 to 1854*, Wilts FHS, 1994.
Jean A. Cole, *Wiltshire County Coroners' Bills 1815-1858,* Wilts FHS, 1997.
Jean A. Cole, *Coroners' Records for Salisbury City:* 1. *1876-92*; 2. *1893-98*; 3. *1899-1901*. Wilts F.H.S.

The National Archives. See page 13 for coroners' records in King's Bench, Assizes and Chancery.

Wiltshire and Swindon Record Office, *Chippenham.*
County. Lists of inquisitions with verdicts, submitted as bills for expenses 1752-1860 (later ones incomplete).
Bills for expenses 1815-58 [A1/705/1-54]
Corsham Liberty. List of inquisitions, with verdicts, submitted as bills for expenses 1761-92 (pubd. Wilts. Record Soc. **36**).
Wootton Bassett Borough. List of inquisitions, with verdicts, submitted as bills for expenses 1765-1792 (pubd. Wilts. Record Soc. **36**).
Marlborough Borough. Inquisitions with orders and lists of witnesses 1773-1835 [G22/1/204]. Published.
Malmesbury. Inquisitions, 1830-54 [G21/1/32] Published.
Bromham. Certificate for burial 1828.
Various areas. Bills 1815-58; expenses 1857-58. Published.

Wiltshire continued

Modern
(asterisked dates usually subject to 75-year closure)

Wiltshire and Swindon Record Office, *Chippenham.*

County. Declarations of office 1890-1913.
Appointments of deputies 1889-1937.
Inquest papers (selected) 1934*-date*.
Register of inquisitions 1921*-date*.
Treasure trove files *c.*1930-date (15-year closure).
Returns and day books *c.*1950*-date*.
Private papers *c.*1930.

Salisbury City. Inquest papers 1876-1974*.
Published 1876-1901.

WORCESTERSHIRE

Medieval

Published
C. Gross (1896) [for JUST 2/206(pt)].

The National Archives [class JUST 2/].
County. Rolls 45-48 Hen III [258], 13-18 Ric II [206], 17-21 Ric II [207].

Sixteenth to Nineteenth Centuries

The National Archives. See page 13 for coroners' records in King's Bench, Assizes and Chancery.

Worcestershire Record Office, *Worcester.*

North Worcestershire. Register of deaths 1956*-1981*[BA10414].
Daily record 1921-58*, 1962-87 [BA08882, 10414].
Case papers 1969*-74* [BA10414].
Post mortem and inquisitions [BA10414].

North East Worcestershire Case papers 1988-94 [BA11043, 11557, 11705, 11979, 12045].

Middle District Daily record 1958-74 [BA11080].
Case papers 1948-74 [BA11080].

South Worcestershire. Jury lists 1844-91 [180 BA 174].
Fee and expenses 1855-74 [183 BA 202/4].
Papers relating to case of Coroner Hughes *v.* County Treasurer and magistrates, 1847-50 [123 BA 168/1].
Annual reports, inquest information and accounts [260:113, temporary deposit].
Additionally, a considerable number of official administrative papers, fees payable, maps and orders.

Worcestershire continued

Worcestershire Record Office, *Worcester.*

Worcester. 'Cravings' (inquests) 1833-35 [Cabinet 9 box 14].
Jurors' books, 1837, 1839-40, 1858-59 and n.d. [Cabinet 9 box 15].
Names of jurors for inquests 1842-53 [Shelf A13 box 2].

Evesham. Four inquest reports 1834-35 [705:739 BA 114iv].

Wyre Piddle. Orders for burial 1846-63 [850 Wyre Piddle BA9089/2iii].

Modern
(asterisked dates usually subject to 75-year closure)

Worcestershire Record Office, *Worcester.*

South Worcestershire. Appointment of deputy coroners 1921-40 [216:254 BA 577].
Sheriffs' returns to writs to summons and fines; jury lists and estreat rolls 1889-1920* [180 BA 731].
Home Office annual returns and statistics 1953*-1974* [260.113, temp. deposit].
Annual reports, inquest information and accounts 1933*-74* [260:113, temp. deposit].
Case papers 1933-74 [BA11539]
Register of deaths reported 1953*-74* [260:113].

South East Division Daily record 1974-79 [BA11080].
Case papers 1974-85 [BA11080, 12027].

Worcestershire Record Office, *Worcester.*

Worcester. Register of inquests 1944*-56* [Cabinet 9 box 15].

Dudley Archives & Local History Service, *Coseley.*

Dudley until 1974, then **Dudley North** and **Dudley South,** 1974-88; Districts amalgamated in 1989 as **Dudley.**

Dudley/Dudley North. Papers, incl. information on deaths, inquisitions and depositions 1940*-1973*, incl. Registers 1966*-73*.

Dudley South. Records 1974*-88*.
Registers 1974*-82*.

Dudley. Records 1989*-94*.

It is believed that earlier records (the borough had a coroner from at least 1826) went for salvage during the war.

YORKSHIRE

Medieval

Published

J.C. Cox, *The Sanctuaries and Sanctuary Seekers of Medieval England* (1911) [for JUST 2/215, mm.1-10(pt)].

C. Gross (1896) [for JUST 2/213(pt), 215(pt), 218(pt), 223(pt), 243,,246, 249,mm.1-2].

W.A. Morris, *The Early English County Court*, Univ. of California Publ. in History **14** [for JUST 2/211(pt)].

The National Archives [class JUST 2/].

County. Rolls 15-16 Ed III [211], 18-19 Ed III [212], 20-22 Ed III [214], 30-33 Ed III [215,mm.39-41], 33-36 Ed III [215,mm.37-38], 36 Ed III [KB 9/141,mm.77,89,90], 36-48 Ed III [218], 37-44 Ed III [217], 38-40 Ed III [220], 43-45 Ed III [224], 44-47 Ed III [225], 46-49 Ed III [227], 48-49 Ed III [228], 49-50 Ed III [230], 49 Ed III - 1 Ric II [232], 50-51 Ed III [231], 1-16 Ric II [236], 5-6 Ric II [239], 6-11 Ric II [240], 7-14 Ric II [241], 12-14 Ric II [245], 12-15 Ric II [246], 13 Ric II [249,m.1], 14-16 Ric II [250]; abstract of several rolls 18-22 Ed III [213] (1341-93).

East Riding. Roll 25,33-36 Ed III [215,mm.11-20] (1351-63).

North Riding. Rolls 14-17 Ed III [210], 15-18 Ed III [209,m.6], 25-36 Ed III [215,mm.21-31] (1340-63).

West Riding. Rolls 16-17 Ed III [209,m.3], 16-18 Ed III [209,m.8], 33-36 Ed III [215,mm.34-36], 40-43 Ed III [222], 49-51 Ed III [229], 51 Ed III - 5 Ric II [233], 1-4 Ric II [235], 9-15 Ric II [242,mm.4-5], 12-16 Ric II [247] (1342-92).

Liberty of the Abbot of St Mary's, York. Rolls 35-36 Ed III [215,m.42], 43-44 Ed III [223], 13-16 Ric II [251] (1369-83).

Liberty of Holderness (Here, the bailiff was also coroner). Rolls 35-36 Ed III [215,m.44,1&2], 51 Ed III - 1 Ric II [234,m.4], 3-13 Ric II [234,m.4], 3-13 Ric II [234,m.1-3], 15-16 Ric II [252] (1361-93).

Liberty of Knaresborough. Rolls 14-17 Ed III [209,m.4], 36 Ed III [215,m.33] (1340-63).

Liberty of Ripon. Roll 11-16 Ric II [244] (1387-93).

Liberty of Ripon outside the town. Roll 7-10 Ed III [209,m.7] (1333-37).

Liberty of St Leonard's Hospital, York. Roll 10,12 Ric II [243] (1386-89).

Liberty of St Peter's, York. Roll 2-9 Ric II [238] (1378-86).

Kingston upon Hull Borough. Roll 12-16 Ric II [248] (1388-93).

Scarborough Borough. Rolls 11-16 Ed III [209,m.5], 31-36 Ed III [215,m.32], 42,44 Ed III, 11-13 Ric II [226], 14,16 Ric II [249,m.2] (1337-93).

Whitby Borough and Liberty of Abbot of Whitby. Roll 30 Ed III - 8 Ric II [216] (1356-85).

York City. Rolls 14-18 Ed III [209,mm.1-2], 23-36 Ed III [2/215,mm.1-10], 36 Ed III - 1 Ric II [219], 2-8 Ric II [237], 9-16 Ric II [242,mm.1-3] (1340-1393).

Sixteenth to Nineteenth Centuries

The National Archives. See page 13 for coroners' records in King's Bench, Assizes and Chancery.

EAST RIDING

East Riding of Yorkshire Archives Office, *Beverley.*

County. Bills for expenses 1752-92 [QSF].

Liberty of Holderness [all DDCC/138]. *c.*61 inquisitions (incl. cause of death, jurors, etc) 1586-1742.

Abstracts of 36 inquisitions 1781-1800.

Book of deodands 1774-89.

Eight inquisitions at York concerning Beverley and Tickton people.

Beverley Borough. Ten inquisitions 1719-30 [DDBC/6/5].

174 inquisitions (incl. jurors) 1754-1811 [DDBC/28].

Single constable's return, Tickton, 1837.

Hull City Archives.

Hull. Depositions and verdicts 1841-99.

University of Hull, Brynmor Jones Library.

Liberty of Howdenshire. Inquisitions 1793-1809 [DX/26/1].

WEST RIDING

Sheffield Archives.

See on-line information.

Sheffield. Coroner's fees and expenses 1873-76 [Bag.C.3440, incl. addresses and causes of death].

Appointments, late 19th century [Bag.C.3444].

Modern

(asterisked dates usually subject to 75-year closure)

Note. In the 1974 boundary reorganisation the three Ridings were replaced by five counties, Cleveland, Humberside and North, South and West Yorkshire; but for convenience post-1974 records are included under the former Ridings.

EAST RIDING

York City Archives Department.

East Riding. Abstracts of inquisitions 1958*-67*.

NORTH RIDING and YORK

Published

P. Hatch, *On View of the Body: Observations of a Coroner* (1986; reminiscences of a Wharfedale coroner).

York City Archives Department.

York City. Inquest books 1935*-71*.

Daily records 1959*-76*.

Abstracts of inquisitions 1958*-68*.

Inquests and reports 1960*-81*.

North Riding. Abstracts of inquisitions 1958*-66*.

North Yorkshire County Record Office, *Northallerton.*
Records are not catalogued, and therefore 'unavailable for consultation'.

Teesside Archives, *Middlesbrough.*
Middlesbrough Borough. Inquest papers 1955*-1968*.
Teesside Borough. Inquest papers 1968*-74*.
Central Cleveland. Inquest papers 1974*-90*.

WEST RIDING

Bradford District Archives.
Bradford. Inquest files, and some financial records 1961*-75* [uncalendared].
Abstract of Inquisitions 1939*-74* [CB1/2/1-2].
Daily record 1940*-77* [CB1/3/1-7].
Miscellaneous registers 1963*-76* [CB1/4/1-4].

Calderdale District Archives, *Halifax.*
Halifax Borough. Inquests 1963*-69* [CO:1-12], 1969*-74* [CO:119-130].
Natural deaths 1966*-68* [CO:13-15], 1971*-73* [CO:131-136].
Declined 1964*-65* [CO:16-17].
Calderdale Borough. Inquests 1975*-76* [CO:137-143].
Natural deaths 1975*-76* [CO:144-147].
Natural deaths and inquests, police copy 1975* [CO:148].
Natural deaths, copies [CO:149].
West Riding County. Inquests 1963*-67*, 1969* [CO:18-42], 1968*-74* [CO:150-187].
Natural deaths 1966*-68* [CO:43-56], 1969*-74* [CO:188-203].
Declined 1963*-65* [CO:57-70].
Daily records 1956*-78* [CO:71-74].
Other records 1966*-76* [CO:204].
Murder files 1971*-73* [CO:205].
Sudden death file 1974* [CO:206].
Post-mortem reports 1954*-62* [CO:76].
Expenditure analysis 1948*-79* [CO:77-102].
Expense sheets 1965*-74* [CO:103-107].
Accounts 1962*-68* [CO:108-110].
Executive Department's copy accounts 1977*-81* [CO:111].
West Yorkshire Police Force standing and general orders 1979*-83* [CO:75].

Doncaster Archives Department.
Doncaster Borough. Reports to the coroner, depositions, inquisitions 1890-1927*.
Daily record 1936*-74* (indexed from 1963).
Doncaster District. Daily record 1932-72 (indexed from 1963).
Rotherham District. Register of deaths reported 1953*-74* (indexed).
South Yorkshire, East District. Daily record 1974 (indexed).
Published: Margaret Wilson, *Inquests and Inquriies: Coroners' Records for the archdeaconry of Doncaster, 1890-1930.* Doncaster & District FHS, 2002.

Kirklees District Archives, *Huddersfield.*
Huddersfield. Inquests 1948*-70*.

North Yorkshire County Record Office, *Northallerton.*
Ripon Liberty. Coroners' records 1855-1917.

Sheffield Archives.
See on-line information.
West Riding. Inquests on Cadeby Colliery explosion 1912 [225/S1/1].
Selected inquests, 1954*-62* [225/S1/2-211].
Barnsley Borough. Registers of inquests 1945*-1971* [547/C6/2-4].
Doncaster Borough. Selected inquests 1931*-74* (incl. Bentley Colliery explosion papers, 1931*) [CC4/F1/1-18].
Rotherham Borough. Inquest books 1931*-54* [546/C524-32].
Returns of inquests 1928*-53* [CC3/D1/1-7].
Deaths reports 1953*-65* [CC3/D2/1].
Sheffield City. Returns 1926*-53* [CC1/D1/1-3].
Deaths reported 1953*-74* [CC1/D2/1-2].
Inquest report books 1940*-53* [CC1/D3/1-18].
Selected inquests 1940*-74* (incl. mining incidents) [CC1/F1-2].
Treasure Trove 1959*-67* [CC1/F4/1].
South Yorkshire West District. Deaths reported 1974*-90* [CC2/D1/1-7] (indexed).
Selected inquests 1975*-84* [CC1/F3-4].
Treasure Trove 1980* [CC2/F3/1].
Papers relating to the Hillsborough incident 1989*-90* [CC5/F1-3].

Leeds. *Published:* Syvia M. Barnard, *Viewing the Breathless Corpse* (2 parts). Three C19 Leeds coroners and 50 inquest reports from Leeds newspapers.

WALES

General

National Library of Wales, *Aberystwyth.*
Inquests are included amongst the Gaol files [Class Wales 4] among the records of the Court of Great Sessions (Assizes), 1543-1830; starting dates vary for each county.

The National Archives. See page 13 for coroners' records in King's Bench, Assizes and Chancery.

ANGLESEY

National Library of Wales, *Aberystwyth.*
Beaumaris. Transcripts of inquisitions 1707 [NLW Ms 6666 D].

Anglesey County Record Office, *Llangefni.*
County. Occasional inquests in Quarter sessions files 1772-1968* (cat'd 1772-1889).
Case files 1968*-94*.

BRECONSHIRE

National Library of Wales, *Aberystwyth.*
County. Occasional inquests in Quarter Sessions rolls/files 1690-1968.

Powys County Archives Office, *Llandrindod Wells.*
Note. All searchers are requested to make appointments well before their intended visits.

County. Ocasional inquests in Quarter sessions files 1690-1968 [B/QS].
South Powys. Records 1974*-89* [Acc 827].
Crickhowell and Tretower. Coroners' papers 1856-1881.

CAERNARVONSHIRE

The county, formerly within the jurisdiction of one coroner, was divided into two during the late nineteenth century.

Caernarfon Record Office, *Caernarfon.*
County. Quarter Sessions Rolls contain coroners' bills for inquests from 1753.

Modern
(asterisked dates usually subject to 75-year closure)

North Caernarvonshire/Caernarfonshire.
Inquests and non-inquest files 1896, 1898-1902, 1951*-77*.
Daily record books 1947*-64*.
Certificates 1973*-77*.
South Caernarvonshire/Caernarfonshire.
Inquest papers 1904-5, 1907-17*, 1923*-57*.
Inquest and non-inquest files 1964*, 1967*-72*, 1978*-81*.
Certificates 1912-57*.
Reports 1914*-23.
Notifications to registrar 1918*-57*.
Orders for burial 1929*-57*.
Letter books 1892-1901.
Correspondence 1904-57*.
Disbursement accounts 1929*-57*.

CARDIGANSHIRE

Cardiganshire/Ceredigion Archives, *Aberystwyth.*
Aberystwyth. Lists of officials, incl. coroners, 1690-1835.

Modern
(asterisked dates usually subject to 75-year closure)

County. Deaths reported 1953*-74*, reports, files re individuals, inquest and non-inquest cases and returns.

CARMARTHENSHIRE

National Library of Wales, *Aberystwyth.*
County. Brief references to inquests in the Calendar Rolls for the then Carmarthen Circuit [Class Wales 7], which can also be used as an index to the Gaol Files (see WALES: General, above).

Modern
(asterisked dates usually subject to 75-year closure)

The earlier districts of Carmarthen Borough and West Carmarthenshire were amalgamated by 1949, and were in turn amalgamated with East Carmarthenshire in 1965, and with the Three Commots (Hundreds), Llanelli Urban and Rural Districts in 1974.

Carmarthenshire Archives Service, *Carmarthen.*
Coroners' records are unlisted. From 1931* (the earliest) they relate to the Three Commots District only; from *c.*1960* they may relate to other districts, and 1974*-87* to the whole of the former county. Records include case files (often with photographs and post-mortem reports).

DENBIGHSHIRE

National Library of Wales, *Aberystwyth.*
County. Letter relating to a contest for coronership 1794 [NLW Ms 12,419 D].
North Denbighshire. Entry book 1874-95 by Evan Pierce MD of Denbigh (1808-95) [MS19702E].

Denbighshire Record Office, *Ruthin.*
County. Inquest papers 1843.
East Denbighshire. Inquest papers 1907-68*.
West Denbighshire. Inquest papers 1937*-74*.
(Asterisked years usually subject to 75-year closure.)

FLINTSHIRE

See also Cheshire, page 19.

Flintshire has had only one coroner; from 1874 Maelor was transferred to the jurisdiction of the Shropshire coroner.

The National Archives.
Maelor Saesneg Commot. Roll 13,15,18 Ed III [CHES 18/1,mm.1-11] (1339-45).
Englefield Cantred. Roll 5 Hen V [CHES 18/1, m.12] (1417-8).

Flintshire Record Office, *Hawarden.*
See on-line information, ref. GB 0208 CR.
(*subject to 75/100-year closure) [CR]
County. Appointments and payment of salaries 1720-1893, 1901-62 [QS/MB Minute/Sessions Books].
Inquisitions and related papers 1818-19, 1848-49, 1916*-69*; East Clwyd district, records 1969-96*, incl sudden death reports 1971-89*, inquest records 1969-96; miscellaneous 1960-68*.
Bills, often incl. names of deceased and verdicts, 1747-1820 [QS/SR].
Receipts for salaries 1820-61 and coroners' bills 1855-59 [QS/FV].

GLAMORGAN

National Library of Wales, *Aberystwyth.*
Letter soliciting support for prospective coroner 1837 [Maybery 2683].

Glamorgan Record Office, *Cardiff.*
General. Return of inquests, Merthyr, Newbridge, Ogmore and Swansea, 1869-75 [Q/S].
Coroner's bills, Epiphany 1876 [Q/S].
Appointment of deputy coroner, 1845 [Q/S].
Coroner's expenses, 1872 [Q/S].
Coroner's notices of deaths, Aberdare and Merthyr, March 1867 - March 1869 [CL MS. 4.806].
Letter re election of coroner, 1832 [D/D Ev 7/38].
Candidature of Hopkin Llewllyn as coroner, 1789-97 [D/D Ll 118].
Expenses for dinner, etc, at election of coroner, 1832 [D/D A 17/19].

Cardiff Central Library.
Cardiff. Inquisitions, deaths, 1767-83 [CL Bute XXX 1/1-85].
Inquisitions, damage, 1775-79 [CL Bute XXX 2/ 1-5].

Glamorgan continued

Modern
(asterisked dates usually subject to 75-year closure)

***Glamorgan Record Office**, Cardiff.*
See information on Cardiff Coroners Records, 1951-1977, on-line.
General. Coroner's vouchers, 1908-18, 1937 [Q/S].
Cardiff. Daily record 1933*-53* [D/D Con C 4/21-24].
Cardiff police inquest books, 1892-1941* [D/D Con C 4/1-20].
Register of deaths 1954*-72* [Cor/C].
Records of inquests 1951*-54*, 1957*-72* [Cor/C].
Aberdare: Post-mortem reports and inquests 1973-1983*.
Merthyr Tydfil. Returns of inquests 1959*-78*.
Register of deaths 1959*-67*.
Notices of death 1978*-87* [all Cor/MT].
East Glamorgan. Register of deaths 1965*-87*.
Death certificate counterfoils, 1955*-60*.
Records of inquests, 1956*-73*.
Notices of death, 1974*-88* (missing Jan-June 1975) [Cor/E].
Misc. papers 1956*-80's*.
Annual returns 1985*-89* [all Cor/E].
North Glamorgan Records of inquests 1944*-85*.
registers of deaths 1953*-61*.
Daily record 1946*-53* [all Cor/N].
South Glamorgan Records of inquests 1973*-77* [Cor/S]

***West Glamorgan Archive Service**, Swansea.*
Neath. Records of inquests, 1944*-46* [Cor/N].
Register of deaths, 1953*-61* [Cor/N].
West Glamorgan. Daily record. 1921*-33* [Cor/N].

MERIONETH

***National Library of Wales,** Aberystwyth.*
County. Roll 10-11 Ed III [Peniarth Ms 405 D] (1336-1338).

***Merioneth Archives/Archifdy Meironnydd Archives,** Dolgellau.*
County. Records, dating from the 1890's, part listed.

Monmouthshire

See under ENGLAND, page 32.

MONTGOMERYSHIRE

***Powys County Archives Office,** Llandrindod Wells.*
Note. All searchers are requested to make appointments well before their intended visits.

County. Inquests occasionally appear on the Quarter Sessions files, 1719-1971* [M/QS].
Inquisitions 1849-50 [COR/1/1-30]; 1948*-57* [COR/1/not numbered] (*asterisked years subject to 75-year closure).

PEMBROKESHIRE

The two former Divisions of the county became the Pembrokeshire Division of Dyfed in April 1974.

***National Library of Wales,** Aberystwyth.*
Haverfordwest. Inquests 1855-58 [MS 3008C].

***Pembrokeshire Record Office,** Haverfordwest.*
(Asterisked years usually subject to 75-year closure.)
Lower Division. Register of deaths reported and inquests held 1886-2001* [T/CR/1/1].
Daily records 1900-87* (except for 1941 and part 1942, almost complete) [T/CR/1/2-36].
Files 1939*, 1947*, 1950*-88* [T/CR/1].
Upper Division. Daily records 1915*-66* [T/CR/2/1-3].
Register of deaths reported 1954*-80* [T/CR/2/4-5].
Correspondence 1968*-75* [T/CR/2/11-18].
Account book 1964*-74* [T/CR/2/20,21].
Bank Statements 1971*-74*.
Files 1932*-45*, 1949*-59*, 1966*-74*.
Counterfoils of notifications to registrar re non-inquests 1965*-75*.
Certificates after inquest 1971*-74* [all T/CR/2].

For post-1974 records, see above.

RADNORSHIRE

***Powys County Archives Office,** Llandrindod Wells.*
Note. All searchers are requested to make appointments well before their intended visits.

County. Occasional inquests in Quarter Sessions files 1753-1968* [R/QS]
Inquisitions, depositions and related papers 1867-73 [R/D/JGW/CR].
Inquisitions and related papers 1869-82 [R/CR].
Reports of deaths, and related papers 1876-82 [R/COR].
Statistical returns 1879-80 [R/CR].
Circulars 1872-73 [R/CR].
Register of deaths reported to the coroner 1953-1975.
South Powys. Records 1974*-89* [Acc 827].